Working Papers
for use with

FUNDAMENTAL ACCOUNTING PRINCIPLES VOLUME 1

SEVENTEENTH CANADIAN EDITION

Kermit D. Larson
University of Texas—Austin

Heidi Dieckmann
Kwantlen Polytechnic University—British Columbia

John Harris
Seneca College—Ontario

Revised by
Laura Dallas
Kwantlen Polytechnic University—British Columbia

Reviewed by
Rhonda Heninger
Southern Alberta Institute of Technology—Alberta

Mc
Graw
Hill

Published by McGraw Hill
145 King Street West, Suite 1501
Toronto, Ontario, Canada, M5H 1J8
Telephone: 1-800-565-5758
Website: www.mheducation.ca

Working Papers for Use with Fundamental Accounting Principles, Volume 1, 17th Canadian Edition
Kermit D. Larson, Heidi Dieckmann, John Harris, Laura Dallas, and Rhonda Heninger

ISBN-13: 978-1-26-088178-3
ISBN-10: 1-26-0881748-4

1 2 3 4 5 6 7 8 9 M 28 27 26 25 24 23 22
Printed and bound in Canada

Director of Product: *Rhondda McNabb*
Senior Portfolio Manager: *Alwynn Pinard*
Marketing Manager: *Rodney Burke*
Content Developers: *Shalini Khanna, Stephanie Schwartz*
Portfolio Associate: *Tracey Hanson*
Senior Supervising Editor: *Janie Deneau*
Plant Production Coordinator: *Heitor Moura*
Manufacturing Production Coordinator: *Jason Stubner*
Cover Design: *Michelle Losier*
Cover Image: *Rachel Idzerda*
Printer: *Maracle Press*

ISBN-13: 978-1-26-088178-3
ISBN-10: 1-26-0881748-4

Contents

Quick Study 1-1

_____
_____
_____
_____
_____
_____
_____
_____
_____
_____
_____
_____

Quick Study 1-2

a. _____

b. _____

c. _____

d. _____

e. _____

Quick Study 1-3

a. _____
b. _____
c. _____
d. _____
e. _____
f. _____

Quick Study 1-4

1.		5.	
2.		6.	
3.		7.	
4.		8.	

Quick Study 1-5

1. _____
2. _____
3. _____
4. _____
5. _____
6. _____
7. _____
8. _____

Quick Study 1-6

_____
_____
_____
_____
_____
_____
_____
_____
_____
_____
_____
_____
_____
_____
_____
_____
_____

Quick Study 1-7

1. _____
2. _____
3. _____

Quick Study 1-8

1. _____
2. _____
3. _____

Quick Study 1-9

	1.	A customer called and made arrangements for Jay's Plumbing to provide $6,000 of services *next month*. Jay, the owner, recorded revenue of $6,000 *this month*. No cash was exchanged.
	2.	Land was purchased for $50,000. The bank appraised it for loan purposes at $68,000. Therefore, the owner of the land recorded it on the balance sheet at $68,000.
	3.	The owner of Dallas Pizza and Don's Deli combines all transactions by keeping only one set of accounting records for both businesses.
	4.	The owner of Miko Japanese Eatery has become ill suddenly and is unable to continue the business. The owner's spouse, in need of cash to finance growing personal expenses, took the business's most recent financial statements to the bank and was granted a loan. She did not inform the bank of her husband's inability to work.
	5.	Dale's Consulting Services completed a contract with an organization located overseas. Dale included the revenue on the income statement without converting the foreign currency to Canadian dollars.

Quick Study 1-10

	1.	Delco performed work for a client located in China and collected 8,450,000 RMB (renminbi, the Chinese currency), the equivalent of about $1,320,000 Canadian. Delco recorded it as 8,450,000.
	2.	Delco collected $180,000 from a customer on December 20, 2023, for work to be done in February 2024. The $180,000 was recorded as revenue during 2023. Delco's year-end is December 31.
	3.	Delco's December 31, 2023, balance sheet showed total assets of $840,000 and liabilities of $1,120,000. The income statements for the past six years have shown a trend of increasing losses.
	4.	Included in Delco's assets was land and a building purchased for $310,000 and reported on the balance sheet at $470,000.
	5.	Delco's owner, Tom Del, consistently buys personal supplies and charges them to the company.

Quick Study 1-11

Assets	=	Liabilities	+	Equity
a.				
b.				
c.				

Quick Study 1-12

	Assets	=	Liabilities	+	Equity
a.					
b.					
c.					

Quick Study 1-13

All-In Servicing
Income Statement
For Month Ended April 30, 2023

Revenues	$300
Expenses	?
Profit (loss)	?

All-In Servicing
Statement of Changes in Equity
For Month Ended April 30, 2023

Tim Allin, capital, April 1		$ 50
Investments by owner	$ 30	
Profit	?	?
Total		$255
Less: Withdrawals by owner		?
Tim Allin, capital, April 30		?

All-In Servicing
Balance Sheet
April 30, 2023

Assets		Liabilities	
Cash	$ 60	Accounts payable	$ 25
Equipment	?	**Equity**	
		Tim Allin, capital	?
		Total liabilities	
Total assets	$265	and equity	?

Quick Study 1-13 (Concluded)

Part b.

All-In Servicing
Income Statement
For Month Ended May 31, 2023

Revenues	?
Expenses..	$ 85
Profit (loss)..	?

All-In Servicing
Statement of Changes in Equity
For Month Ended May 31, 2023

Tim Allin, capital, May 1		?
Investments by owner	$ 60	
Profit	?	$110
Total		?
Less: Withdrawals by owner		75
Tim Allin, capital, May 31		?

All-In Servicing
Balance Sheet
May 31, 2023

Assets		**Liabilities**	
Cash	$120	Accounts payable	$ 45
Equipment	?	**Equity**	
		Tim Allin, capital	?
		Total liabilities	
Total assets	?	and equity	?

Quick Study 1-14

1. _____

2. _____
_____
_____

Quick Study 1-15

Assets	=	Liabilities	+	Equity
a.				
b.				
c.				
d.				
e.				

Quick Study 1-16

_____	1. Supplies		_____	8. Utilities expense
_____	2. Supplies expense		_____	9. Furniture
_____	3. Accounts receivable		_____	10. Revenue
_____	4. Accounts payable		_____	11. Rent revenue
_____	5. Equipment		_____	12. Salaries expense
_____	6. Tim Roadster's withdrawals	_____		13. Tim Roadster's investments
_____	7. Notes payable		_____	14. Profit

Quick Study 1-17

_____   1. Total revenues
_____   2. Total operating expenses
_____   3. Profit
_____   4. Total assets
_____   5. Total liabilities
_____   6. Tim Roadster, capital (April 30, 2023)
_____   7. Total liabilities and equity

Quick Study 1-18

_____	1.	Loss	$ ____	_____
_____	2.	Rent expense	22	_____
_____	3.	Rent payable	6	_____
_____	4.	Accounts receivable	14	_____
_____	5.	Paul Sangha's investments in May	30	_____
_____	6.	Interest income	2	_____
_____	7.	Paul Sangha's, capital, May 1, 2023	0	_____
_____	8.	Repair supplies	5	_____
_____	9.	Notes payable	25	_____
_____	10.	Paul Sangha's withdrawals in May	5	_____
_____	11.	Truck	15	_____
_____	12.	Consulting revenue	18	_____
_____	13.	Paul Sangha, capital, May 31, 2023	____	_____
_____	14.	Cash	20	_____

Name: _____

Quick Study 1-19

Income Statement

Statement of Changes in Equity

Balance Sheet

Quick Study 1-20

_____
_____
_____
_____

Quick Study 1-21

Assets	=	Liabilities	+	Equity
1.				
2.				

Quick Study 1-22

	1.	Assets
	2.	Cash from operating activities
	3.	Equipment
	4.	Expenses
	5.	Liabilities
	6.	Net decrease (or increase) in cash
	7.	Revenues
	8.	Total liabilities and equities

Quick Study 1-23

	1.	Land
	2.	Wages payable
	3.	Equipment
	4.	Accounts payable
	5.	Accounts receivable
	6.	Supplies

Fundamental Accounting Principles, 17ce, Working Papers   9

Exercise 1-1

a. _____

b. _____

c. _____

d. _____

e. _____

f. _____

g. _____

Exercise 1-2

External Users	Decisions
1.	
2.	
3.	
4.	

Internal Users	Decisions
1.	
2.	
3.	
4.	

Name: _____

Exercise 1-3

Accounting Role	Typical Day
(1) External auditor	
(2) Controller	
(3) Tax Specialist	

Name: _____

Exercise 1-4

a. _____

_____

_____

_____

_____

_____

_____

_____

_____

_____

b. _____

_____

_____

_____

_____

_____

_____

_____

_____

_____

_____

_____

_____

c. _____

_____

_____

_____

_____

_____

_____

_____

_____

_____

_____

_____

_____

Fundamental Accounting Principles, 17ce, Working Papers

Exercise 1-5

1.	_____
2.	_____
3.	_____
4.	_____

Exercise 1-6

	1.	A company reports details behind financial statements that would impact users' decisions.
	2.	Financial statements reflect the assumption that the business continues operating.
	3.	A company records the expenses incurred to generate the revenues reported.
	4.	Concepts, assumptions, and guidelines for preparing financial statements
	5.	Each business is accounted for separately from its owner or owners.
	6.	Revenue is recorded when products and services are delivered.
	7.	Detailed rules used in reporting events and transactions.
	8.	Information is based on actual costs incurred in transactions.

Balance Sheet			Income Statement		Statement of Changes in Equity
Assets	Liabilities	Owner's Equity	Revenue	Expenses	

Chapter 1

Exercise 1-8

a. _____

b. _____

c. _____

_____

_____

d. _____

_____

_____

Exercise 1-9

	(a)	(b)	(c)	(d)	(e)
Equity, January 1	$ -0-	$ -0-	$ -0-	$ -0-	
Owner's investments during the year	60,000		31,500	37,500	140,000
Profit (loss) for the year	15,750	30,500	(4,500)		(8,000)
Owner's withdrawals during the year		(27,000)	(20,000)	(15,750)	(63,000)
Equity, December 31	56,000	49,500		32,000	171,000

Exercise 1-10

Income Statement

Exercise 1-11

Statement of Changes in Equity

Analysis component:

Balance Sheet

Analysis component:

_____

_____

_____

_____

_____

Exercise 1-13

Income Statement

Exercise 1-14

Statement of Changes in Equity

Analysis component:

Name: _____

Balance Sheet

Analysis component:

_____
_____
_____
_____
_____

Name: _____

Exercise 1-16

(a) Profit (Loss) =

    Supporting Calculations:

_____

_____

_____

_____

_____

_____

_____

(b) Profit (Loss) =

    Supporting Calculations:

_____

_____

_____

_____

_____

_____

_____

(c) Profit (Loss) =

    Supporting Calculations:

_____

_____

_____

_____

_____

_____

_____

(d) Profit (Loss) =

    Supporting Calculations:

_____

_____

_____

_____

_____

_____

Chapter 1   Name: _____

Exercise 1-17

(a) Assets =
  Equity = | |
  Supporting Calculations: _____

_____

_____

_____

_____

_____

(b) Liabilities =
  Equity = | |
  Supporting Calculations: _____

_____

_____

_____

_____

_____

Exercise 1-18

	ASSETS			=	LIABILITIES	+	EQUITY
CASH	+ ACCOUNTS RECEIVABLE	+	OFFICE SUPPLIES	=	ACCOUNTS PAYABLE	+	KATIE COPP, CAPITAL
(a)							
(b)							
(c)							
(d)							
(e)							
(f)							

Name: _____

Exercise 1-19

	ASSETS				=	LIABILITIES	+	EQUITY
CASH	+ ACCOUNTS RECEIVABLE	+ PARTS SUPPLIES	+ EQUIPMENT	=		ACCOUNTS PAYABLE	+	STACEY COMEAU, CAPITAL
(a)								
(b)								
(c)								
(d)								
(e)								
(f)								
(g)								
(h)								
(i)								

Exercise 1-20

a. _____

b. _____

c. _____

d. _____

e. _____

f. _____

g. _____

		ASSETS				LIABILITIES	+	EQUITY	
CASH	+	ACCOUNTS RECEIVABLE	+	SUPPLIES	+	EQUIP-MENT	=	ACCOUNTS PAYABLE	+	MAILIN MOON, CAPITA	EXPLANATION OF EQUITY TRANSACTIO
(a)									
(b)									
(c)									
(d)									
(e)									
(f)									
(g)									

Exercise 1-22

Mailin Moon – Freelance Writing
Income Statement
For Month Ended March 31, 2023

Revenues:
   Freelance writing revenue ....
Operating expenses:
   Salaries expense..
   Rent expense.. _____
     Total operating expenses... _____
Profit... _____

Mailin Moon – Freelance Writing
Statement of Changes in Equity
For Month Ended March 31, 2023

Mailin Moon, capital, March 1..
Add: Investment by owner..
Profit .... _____
Mailin Moon, capital, March 31.. _____

Mailin Moon – Freelance Writing
Balance Sheet
March 31, 2023

Assets	Liabilities
Cash	Accounts payable.....................................
....	
....	
Accounts receivable.....	
Supplies......................	
Equipment	
	Equity
	Mailin Moon, capital............................ _____
Total assets .... _____	Total liabilities and equity..................... _____

Analysis component:

_____
_____
_____
_____
_____
_____
_____
_____

	ASSETS			=	LIABILITIES	+	EQUITY	
CASH	+	ACCOUNTS RECEIVABLE	+ SUPPLIES	+	EQUIP- MENT	=	ACCOUNTS PAYABLE	+	ALI OMAR, CAPITAL	EXPLANATION OF EQUITY TRANSACTION
(a)									
(b)									
(c)									
(d)									
(e)									
(f)									
(g)									
(h)									
(i)									

Exercise 1-24

Income Statement

Statement of Changes in Equity

Balance Sheet

Name: _____

Exercise 1-24 (Concluded)

Analysis component:

_____

_____

_____

_____

_____

_____

_____

_____

_____

_____

ASSETS				=	LIABILITIES	+	EQUITY	
CASH	+	ACCOUNTS RECEIVABLE	+	SUPPLIES	+	EQUIP-MENT	=	ACCOUNTS PAYABLE	+	NATALIE GOLD, CAPITAL	EXPLANATION OF EQUITY TRANSACTION
Bal.$6,000		$1,200		$1,900		$6,500		$4,000		$11,600	
(a)											
(b)											
(c)											
(d)											
(e)											
(f)											
(g)											
(h)											

Name: _____

Exercise 1-26

Income Statement		

Statement of Changes in Equity		

Name: _____

Exercise 1-26 (Concluded)

Balance Sheet			

Analysis component:

_____
_____
_____
_____
_____

Chapter 1   Name: _____

Problem 1-1A

Characteristic	Type of Business Organization		
	Sole Proprietorship	Partnership	Corporation
Limited liability			
Unlimited liability			
Owners are shareholders			
Owners are partners			
Taxed as a separate legal entity			

Problem 1-2A

EMAIL

To: _____
From: _____
Subject: _____

_____
_____
_____
_____
_____
_____
_____
_____
_____
_____
_____
_____
_____
_____
_____
_____
_____
_____
_____
_____
_____
_____
_____
_____
_____

Name: _____

Problem 1-3A

2022 Profit (Loss) = [   ]
    Supporting Calculations: _____

_____
_____
_____
_____
_____
_____
_____
_____
_____

Problem 1-4A

_____

Income Statement

Problem 1-4A (Concluded)

Statement of Changes in Equity

Balance Sheet

Analysis component:

_____

_____

_____

_____

_____

Problem 1-5A

Income Statement

Statement of Changes in Equity

Fundamental Accounting Principles, 17ce, Working Papers

Problem 1 5A (Concluded)

Balance Sheet

Analysis component:

_____

_____

_____

_____

_____

_____

Problem 1-6A

Part 1

Balance Sheet

Problem 1-6A (Concluded)

Balance Sheet			

Part 2

Profit (Loss) Calculation: _____

_____

_____

_____

_____

_____

_____

_____

_____

_____

_____

Analysis component:

_____

_____

_____

_____

_____

_____

_____

_____

Problem 1-7A

Part 1: Company A

(a) _____

_____

_____

_____

(b) _____

_____

_____

_____

_____

_____

_____

(c) _____

_____

_____

_____

_____

_____

Part 2: Company B

(a) _____

_____

_____

_____

(b) _____

_____

_____

_____

_____

(c) _____

_____

_____

_____

Name: _____

Problem 1-7A (Continued)

Part 3: Company C

_____
_____
_____
_____
_____
_____
_____
_____
_____
_____
_____
_____
_____
_____
_____

Part 4: Company D

_____
_____
_____
_____
_____
_____
_____
_____
_____
_____
_____
_____
_____
_____
_____
_____
_____

Name: _____

Problem 1-7A (Concluded)

Part 5: Company E

_____
_____
_____
_____
_____
_____
_____
_____
_____
_____
_____
_____
_____
_____
_____
_____

Problem 1-8A

Parts 1 and 2

	ASSETS				=	LIABILITIES	+	+	EQUITY
CASH +	ACCOUNTS + RECEIVABLE	OFFICE + SUPPLIES	OFFICE + EQUIPMENT	BUILDING =		ACCOUNTS + PAYABLE	NOTES PAYABLE	GEORGE LITTLECHILD, CAPITAL	EXPLANATION OF EQUITY TRANSACTION
(a)									
(b)									
Bal.									
(c)									
Bal.									
(d)									
Bal.									
(e)									
Bal.									
(f)									
Bal.									
(g)									
Bal.									
(h)									
Bal.									
(i)									
Bal.									
(j)									
Bal.									
(k)									
Bal.									
(l)									
Bal.									

Name: _____

Problem 1-8A (Concluded)

Part 3

Littlechild Enterprises
Income Statement
For Month Ended March 31, 2023

Revenues :
    Service revenue..

Operating expenses:
    Wages expense..
    Advertising expense..
        Total operating expenses..
Loss..

Littlechild Enterprises
Statement of Changes in Equity
For Month Ended March 31, 2023

George Littlechild, capital, March 1
Add: Investment by owner
    Total
Less: Withdrawal by owner
Loss
George Littlechild, capital, March 31

Littlechild Enterprises
Balance Sheet
March 31, 2023

Assets		Liabilities	
Cash		Accounts payable	
Accounts receivable		Notes payable	
Office supplies		Total liabilities	
Office equipment			
Building			
		Equity	
		George Littlechild, capital	
Total assets		Total liabilities and equity	

Analysis component:

_____
_____
_____
_____
_____
_____
_____

Problem 1-9A

DATE	ASSETS					=	LIABILITIES	+	EQUITY	
	CASH	+ ACCOUNTS RECEIVABLE	+ OFFICE SUPPLIES	+ OFFICE EQUIPMENT	+ ELECTRICAL EQUIPMENT	=	ACCOUNTS PAYABLE	+	LARRY POWER, CAPITAL	EXPLANATION OF EQUITY TRANSACTION

Problem 1-9A (Concluded)

Analysis component:

_____
_____
_____
_____
_____
_____

Problem 1-10A

Income Statement

Statement of Changes in Equity

Problem 1-10A (Concluded)

	Balance Sheet		

Analysis component:
_____
_____
_____
_____
_____
_____

Problem 1-11A

	TRANSACTION	BALANCE SHEET			INCOME STATEMENT
		TOTAL ASSETS	TOTAL LIABILITIES	EQUITY	PROFIT
1.	Owner invests cash				
2.	Sell services for cash				
3.	Acquire services on credit				
4.	Pay wages with cash				
5.	Owner withdraws cash				
6.	Borrow cash with note payable				
7.	Sell services on credit				
8.	Buy office equipment for cash				
9.	Collect receivable from (7)				
10.	Buy asset with note payable				

Income Statement		

Name: _____

Problem 1-4B (Concluded)

Statement of Changes in Equity

Balance Sheet

Analysis component:

_____
_____
_____
_____
_____

2022 Profit (Loss) = ☐
    Supporting Calculations: _____

_____
_____
_____
_____
_____
_____
_____
_____
_____

Problem 1-4B

_____

Income Statement

Name: _____

Problem 1-4B (Concluded)

Statement of Changes in Equity

Balance Sheet

Analysis component:

_____

_____

_____

_____

_____

Income Statement

Problem 1-5B (Concluded)

Statement of Changes in Equity

Balance Sheet

Analysis component:

_____

_____

_____

_____

_____

Problem 1-5B

Income Statement		

Name: _____

Problem 1-6B (Concluded)

Part 2

Profit (Loss) Calculation: _____

_____
_____
_____
_____
_____
_____
_____
_____
_____
_____
_____

Analysis component: _____

_____
_____
_____
_____
_____
_____

Problem 1-7B

Part 1: Company V

(a) _____

_____
_____
_____

(b) _____

_____
_____
_____

(c) _____

_____
_____
_____
_____

Problem 1-7B (Continued)

Part 2: Company W

(a) _____
_____
_____
_____

(b) _____
_____
_____
_____
_____
_____
_____
_____

(c) _____
_____
_____
_____
_____
_____
_____
_____

Part 3: Company X

_____
_____
_____
_____
_____
_____
_____
_____
_____
_____
_____
_____
_____
_____
_____

Name: _____

Problem 1-8B (Concluded)

Part 3

Zhang Consulting
Income Statement
For Year Ended December 31, 2023

Revenues:
    Consulting services revenue...
Operating expenses:
    Wages expense...
    Advertising expense...
        Total operating expenses...
Profit...

Zhang Consulting
Statement of Changes in Equity
For Year Ended December 31, 2023

Lily Zhang, capital, January 1
Add: Investments by owner
Profit
    Total
Less: Withdrawals by owner
Lily Zhang, capital, December 31

Zhang Consulting
Balance Sheet
December 31, 2023

Assets	Liabilities
Cash	Accounts payable
Accounts receivable	Notes payable
Office supplies	Total liabilities
Office equipment	
Building	**Equity**
	Lily Zhang, capital
Total assets	Total liabilities and equity

Analysis component:

_____
_____
_____
_____
_____
_____
_____
_____

Name: _____

Problem 1-8B (Parts 1 and 2)

	ASSETS					=	LIABILITIES		+	EQUITY	
CASH	+ ACCOUNTS RECEIVABLE	+ OFFICE SUPPLIES	+ OFFICE EQUIPMENT	+ BUILDING		=	= ACCOUNTS PAYABLE	+ NOTES PAYABLE	+	LILY ZHANG, CAPITAL	EXPLANATION OF EQUITY TRANSACTION
(a)											
(b)											
Bal.											
(c)											
Bal.											
(d)											
Bal.											
(e)											
Bal.											
(f)											
Bal.											
(g)											
Bal.											
(h)											
Bal.											
(i)											
Bal.											
(j)											
Bal.											
(k)											
Bal.											
(l)											
Bal.											

Name: _____

Problem 1-8B (Concluded)

Part 3

Zhang Consulting
Income Statement
For Year Ended December 31, 2023

Revenues:
    Consulting services revenue...
Operating expenses:
    Wages expense..
    Advertising expense.. _____
       Total operating expenses..
Profit...

Zhang Consulting
Statement of Changes in Equity
For Year Ended December 31, 2023

Lily Zhang, capital, January 1
Add: Investments by owner
Profit
    Total
Less: Withdrawals by owner
Lily Zhang, capital, December 31

Zhang Consulting
Balance Sheet
December 31, 2023

Assets		Liabilities	
Cash		Accounts payable	
Accounts receivable		Notes payable	
Office supplies		Total liabilities	
Office equipment			
Building		Equity	
		Lily Zhang, capital	
Total assets		Total liabilities and equity	

Analysis component:

_____
_____
_____
_____
_____
_____
_____
_____

Name: _____

Problem 1-9B

DATE	CASH	+ ACCOUNTS RECEIVABLE	+ OFFICE SUPPLIES	ASSETS + EVENT EQUIPMENT	+ SOUND SYSTEM EQUIPMENT	= LIABILITIES = ACCOUNTS PAYABLE	+ EQUITY + MICHAEL CANTU, CAPITAL	EXPLANATION OF EQUITY TRANSACTION

Problem 1-9B (Concluded)

Analysis component: _____

_____

_____

_____

_____

_____

_____

Problem 1-10B

Income Statement

Problem 1-9B

| DATE | ASSETS | | | | | = | LIABILITIE | + | EQUITY | |
	CASH	+ ACCOUNTS RECEIVABLE	+ OFFICE SUPPLIES	+ EVENT EQUIPMENT	+ SOUND SYSTEM EQUIPMENT	=	ACCOUNTS PAYABLE	+	MICHAEL CANTU, CAPITAL	EXPLANATION OF EQUITY TRANSACTION

Problem 1-11B

TRANSACTION		BALANCE SHEET		INCOME STATEMENT
	TOTAL ASSETS	TOTAL LIABILITIES	EQUITY	PROFIT
1. Owner invests cash				
2. Pay wages with cash				
3. Acquire services on credit				
4. Buy store equipment for cash				
5. Borrow cash with note payable				
6. Sell services for cash				
7. Sell services on credit				
8. Pay rent with cash				
9. Owner withdraws cash				
10. Collect receivable from (7)				

Problem 1-12B

Income Statement		

Fundamental Accounting Principles, 17ce, Working Papers

Name: _____

Quick Study 2-1

1. _____	Buildings	16. _____ Unearned Subscription Revenue
2. _____	Building Repair Expense	17. _____ Prepaid Subscription Fees
3. _____	Wages Expense	18. _____ Supplies
4. _____	Wages Payable	19. _____ Supplies Expense
5. _____	Notes Receivable	20. _____ Rent Revenue
6. _____	Notes Payable	21. _____ Unearned Rent Revenue
7. _____	Prepaid Advertising	22. _____ Prepaid Rent
8. _____	Advertising Expense	23. _____ Rent Payable
9. _____	Advertising Payable	24. _____ Service Revenue
10. _____	Unearned Advertising	25. _____ Jessica Vuong, Withdrawals
11. _____	Advertising Revenue	26. _____ Jessica Vuong, Capital
12. _____	Interest Income	27. _____ Salaries Expense
13. _____	Interest Expense	28. _____ Salaries Payable
14. _____	Interest Payable	29. _____ Furniture
15. _____	Subscription Revenue	30. _____ Equipment

Quick Study 2-7

	Date	Account Titles and Explanation		Debit	Credit
a.					
b.					
c.					
d.					
e.					

Quick Study 2-6

a.	Analysis	
	Journal entry analysis	
b.	Analysis	
	Journal entry analysis	
c.	Analysis	
	Journal entry analysis	
d.	Analysis	
	Journal entry analysis	
e.	Analysis	
	Journal entry analysis	

Name: _____

Quick Study 2-7

	Date	Account Titles and Explanation		Debit	Credit
a.					
b.					
c.					
d.					
e.					

Fundamental Accounting Principles, 17ce, Working Papers

Name: _____

Quick Study 2-8

Part 1 and 2

Cash			
Jul 31	25,000		

Accounts Receivable			
Jul 31	1,500		

Furniture			
Jul 31	5,000		

Accounts Payable			
		500	Jul 31

Douglas Malone, Capital			
		28,000	Jul. 31

Revenue			
		4,500	Jul. 31

Cleaning Expense			
Jul. 31	1,500		

Part 3

_____
_____
_____
_____

Name: _____

Quick Study 2-9

May 2	Analysis				
	Journal entry analysis				
	Journal Entry				
	Date	Account Titles and Explanation		Debit	Credit

May 10	Analysis				
	Journal entry analysis				
	Journal Entry				
	Date	Account Titles and Explanation		Debit	Credit

May 12	Analysis				
	Journal entry analysis				
	Journal Entry				
	Date	Account Titles and Explanation		Debit	Credit

Chapter 2

Quick Study 2-8

Part 1 and 2

	Cash	
Jul 31	25,000	

	Accounts Receivable	
Jul 31	1,500	

	Furniture	
Jul 31	5,000	

	Accounts Payable	
	500	Jul 31

	Douglas Malone, Capital	
	28,000	Jul. 31

	Revenue	
	4,500	Jul. 31

	Cleaning Expense	
Jul. 31	1,500	

Part 3

_____
_____
_____
_____

Chapter 2

Quick Study 2-10

Parts 1 and 2

Cash			
Apr. 30	15,000		

Accounts Receivable			
Apr. 30	3,200		

Car			

Accounts Payable			
		6,000	Apr. 30

Unearned Revenue			
		1,800	Apr. 30

Dee Bell, Capital			
		8,900	Apr. 30

Revenue			
		3,000	Apr. 30

Wages Expense			
Apr. 30	1,500		

Part 3

_____

_____

_____

_____

Fundamental Accounting Principles, 17ce, Working Papers

Chapter 2

Quick Study 2-11

Accounts Receivable

1,000	650
400	920
920	1,500
3,000	

Accounts Payable

250	250
900	1,800
650	1,400
	650

Service Revenue

	13,000
	2,500
	810
	3,500

Utilities Expense

610	
520	
390	
275	

Cash

3,900	2,400
17,800	3,900
14,500	21,800
340	

Notes Payable

4,000	50,000
8,000	

Name: _____

Quick Study 2-14

Cash   ACCOUNT NO. ____

DATE	EXPLANATION	PR	DEBIT	CREDIT	BALANCE

Office Supplies   ACCOUNT NO. ____

DATE	EXPLANATION	PR	DEBIT	CREDIT	BALANCE

Equipment   ACCOUNT NO. ____

DATE	EXPLANATION	PR	DEBIT	CREDIT	BALANCE

Accounts Payable   ACCOUNT NO. ____

DATE	EXPLANATION	PR	DEBIT	CREDIT	BALANCE

Stan Adams, Capital   ACCOUNT NO. ____

DATE	EXPLANATION	PR	DEBIT	CREDIT	BALANCE

Landscaping Services Revenue   ACCOUNT NO. ____

DATE	EXPLANATION	PR	DEBIT	CREDIT	BALANCE

Name: _____

GENERAL JOURNAL

Date	Account Titles and Explanation	PR	Debit	Credit

Quick Study 2-14

Cash   ACCOUNT NO. ____

DATE	EXPLANATION	PR	DEBIT	CREDIT	BALANCE

Office Supplies   ACCOUNT NO. ____

DATE	EXPLANATION	PR	DEBIT	CREDIT	BALANCE

Equipment   ACCOUNT NO. ____

DATE	EXPLANATION	PR	DEBIT	CREDIT	BALANCE

Accounts Payable   ACCOUNT NO. ____

DATE	EXPLANATION	PR	DEBIT	CREDIT	BALANCE

Stan Adams, Capital   ACCOUNT NO. ____

DATE	EXPLANATION	PR	DEBIT	CREDIT	BALANCE

Landscaping Services Revenue   ACCOUNT NO. ____

DATE	EXPLANATION	PR	DEBIT	CREDIT	BALANCE

Quick Study 2-15

Trial Balance		
	Debit	Credit

Quick Study 2-16

_____

_____

_____

_____

_____

Quick Study 2-17

_____

_____

_____

_____

_____

_____

Quick Study 2-18

_____

_____

_____

_____

_____

_____

_____

Name: _____

Exercise 2-1

		(a) Basic Account	(b) Financial Statement	(c) Normal Balance	(d) Effect of a Debit	(e) Effect of a Credit
a.	Cash					
b.	Supplies					
c.	Accounts Payable					
d.	Yoojin Chang, Capital Account					
e.	Yoojin Chang, Withdrawals					
f.	Design Revenue					
g.	Salaries Expense					
h.	Accounts Receivable					
i.	Notes Payable					
j.	Prepaid insurance					

Name: _____

Quick Study 2-15

Trial Balance		
	Debit	Credit

Quick Study 2-16

Quick Study 2-17

Quick Study 2-18

Name: _____

Exercise 2-3

	Date	Account Titles and Explanation		Debit	Credit
a.					
b.					
c.					
d.					
e.					
f.					
g.					

Chapter 2

Exercise 2-4

Parts 1 and 2

Cash 101	Accounts Receivable 106	Equipment 161

Accounts Payable 201	Christina Reis, Capital 301	Revenue 403

Part 3

_____
_____
_____
_____
_____
_____
_____

Name: _____

Exercise 2-5

a.	Analysis				
	Journal entry analysis				
	Journal Entry				
	Date	**Account Titles and Explanation**		**Debit**	**Credit**

b.	Analysis				
	Journal entry analysis				
	Journal Entry				
	Date	**Account Titles and Explanation**		**Debit**	**Credit**

c.	Analysis				
	Journal entry analysis				
	Journal Entry				
	Date	**Account Titles and Explanation**		**Debit**	**Credit**

Exercise 2-5 (cont'd.)

d.	Analysis	
	Journal entry analysis	
	Journal Entry	

Date	Account Titles and Explanation		Debit	Credit

e.	Analysis	
	Journal entry analysis	
	Journal Entry	

Date	Account Titles and Explanation		Debit	Credit

f.	Analysis	
	Journal entry analysis	
	Journal Entry	

Date	Account Titles and Explanation		Debit	Credit

Exercise 2-5 (concl'd.)

g.	Analysis				
	Journal entry analysis				
	Journal Entry				
	Date	Account Titles and Explanation		Debit	Credit

h.	Analysis				
	Journal entry analysis				
	Journal Entry				
	Date	Account Titles and Explanation		Debit	Credit

i.	Analysis				
	Journal entry analysis				
	Journal Entry				
	Date	Account Titles and Explanation		Debit	Credit

Cash		Accounts Payable	

Accounts Receivable		William Curtis, Capital	

Office Supplies		William Curtis, Withdrawals	

Office Equipment		Revenue	

		Rent Expense	

Name: _____

Exercise 2-7

GENERAL JOURNAL   Page____

Trans.	Account Titles and Explanation	PR	Debit	Credit

Transactions not creating revenue and the reasons:

_____
_____
_____
_____
_____
_____
_____
_____
_____
_____
_____
_____
_____

Exercise 2-8

GENERAL JOURNAL   Page____

Date	Account Titles and Explanation	PR	Debit	Credit

Exercise 2-8 (concl'd.)

Transactions not creating revenue and the reasons:

_____
_____
_____
_____
_____
_____
_____
_____
_____
_____
_____
_____
_____
_____
_____
_____

Exercise 2-9

Parts 1 and 3

Note: T-accounts may be used or the balance column format; both are provided for in Parts 1 and 3 of this exercise.

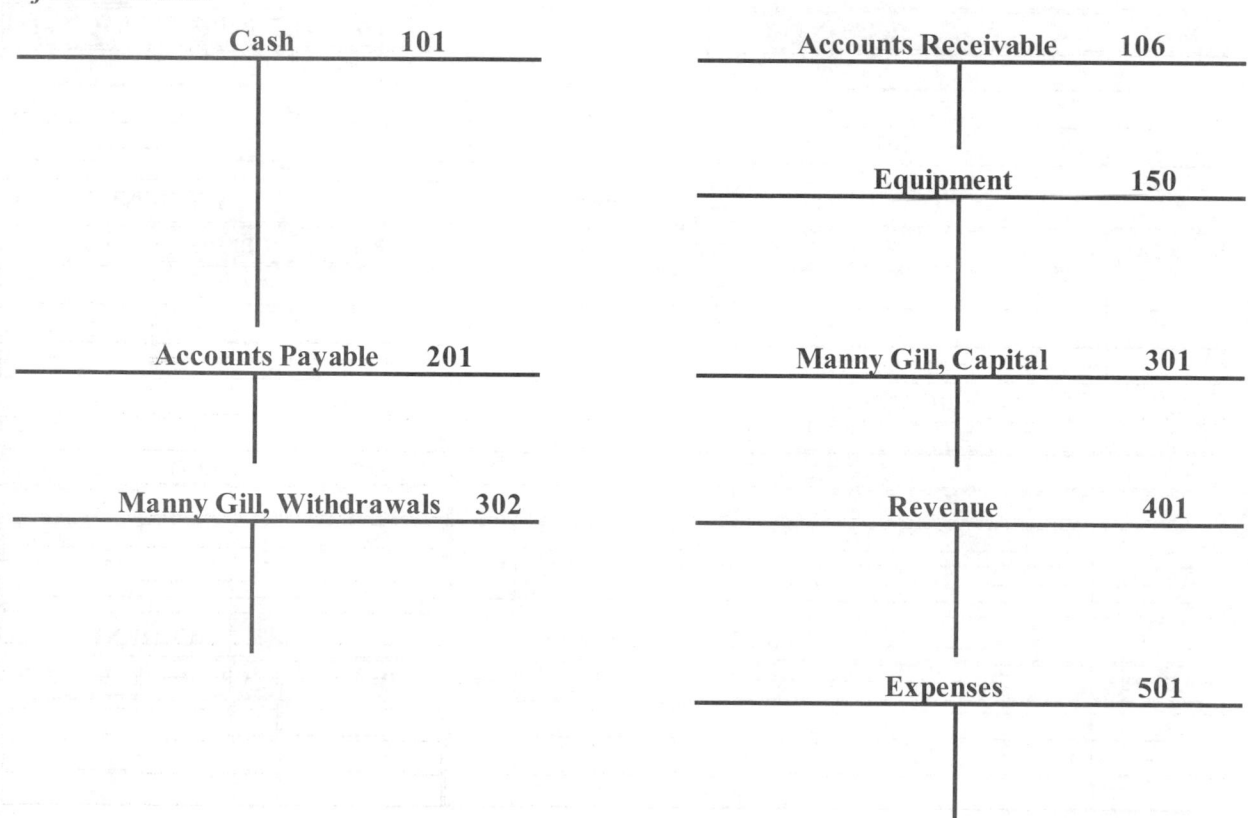

Exercise 2-9 (cont'd.)

Note: T-accounts may be used or the balance column format; both are provided for in Parts 1 and 3 of this exercise.

GENERAL LEDGER

Cash   ACCOUNT NO. 101

DATE	EXPLANATION	PR	DEBIT	CREDIT	BALANCE

Accounts Receivable   ACCOUNT NO. 106

DATE	EXPLANATION	PR	DEBIT	CREDIT	BALANCE

Equipment   ACCOUNT NO. 150

DATE	EXPLANATION	PR	DEBIT	CREDIT	BALANCE

Accounts Payable   ACCOUNT NO. 201

DATE	EXPLANATION	PR	DEBIT	CREDIT	BALANCE

Manny Gill, Capital   ACCOUNT NO. 301

DATE	EXPLANATION	PR	DEBIT	CREDIT	BALANCE

Manny Gill, Withdrawals   ACCOUNT NO. 302

DATE	EXPLANATION	PR	DEBIT	CREDIT	BALANCE

Exercise 2-9 (cont'd.)

Revenue   ACCOUNT NO. 401

DATE	EXPLANATION	PR	DEBIT	CREDIT	BALANCE

Expenses   ACCOUNT NO. 501

DATE	EXPLANATION	PR	DEBIT	CREDIT	BALANCE

Part 2

GENERAL JOURNAL   Page____

Date	Account Titles and Explanation	PR	Debit	Credit

Exercise 2-9 (cont'd.)

GENERAL JOURNAL   Page____

Date	Account Titles and Explanation	PR	Debit	Credit

Part 4

West Secure
Trial Balance
July 31, 2023

Acct. No.	Account Title	Debit	Credit

Part 5

West Secure
Income Statement
For Month Ended July 31, 2023

Revenue		
Expenses		
Profit		

Exercise 2-9 (concl'd.)

<table>
<tr><td colspan="3" align="center">West Secure</td></tr>
<tr><td colspan="3" align="center">Statement of Changes in Equity</td></tr>
<tr><td colspan="3" align="center">For Month Ended July 31, 2023</td></tr>
<tr><td>Manny Gill, capital, July 1</td><td></td><td></td></tr>
<tr><td>Add: Investments by owner</td><td></td><td></td></tr>
<tr><td>Profit</td><td></td><td></td></tr>
<tr><td>   Total</td><td></td><td></td></tr>
<tr><td>Less: Withdrawals by owner</td><td></td><td></td></tr>
<tr><td>Manny Gill, capital, July 31</td><td></td><td></td></tr>
<tr><td></td><td></td><td></td></tr>
</table>

<table>
<tr><td colspan="4" align="center">West Secure</td></tr>
<tr><td colspan="4" align="center">Balance Sheet</td></tr>
<tr><td colspan="4" align="center">July 31, 2023</td></tr>
<tr><td colspan="2" align="center">Assets</td><td colspan="2" align="center">Liabilities</td></tr>
<tr><td>Cash</td><td></td><td>Accounts payable</td><td></td></tr>
<tr><td>Accounts receivable</td><td></td><td colspan="2" align="center">Equity</td></tr>
<tr><td>Equipment</td><td></td><td>Manny Gill, capital</td><td></td></tr>
<tr><td>Total assets</td><td></td><td>Total liabilities and equity</td><td></td></tr>
<tr><td></td><td></td><td></td><td></td></tr>
<tr><td></td><td></td><td></td><td></td></tr>
<tr><td></td><td></td><td></td><td></td></tr>
</table>

Analysis component:

_____

_____

_____

_____

_____

_____

_____

_____

_____

_____

_____

_____

_____

Exercise 2-10

Account Number	Account Name	Account Number	Account Name
_____	Cash	_____	Aaron Paquette, Withdrawals
_____	Accounts Receivable	_____	Consulting Revenues
_____	Office Equipment	_____	Salaries Expense
_____	Accounts Payable	_____	Rent Expense
_____	Unearned Revenue	_____	Utilities Expense
_____	Aaron Paquette, Capital		

Exercise 2-11 Part 1

GENERAL JOURNAL   Page____

Date	Account Titles and Explanation	PR	Debit	Credit

Exercise 2-11 (cont'd.)

Part 2

Cash		101
Bal.	15,000	

Accounts Receivable		115
Bal.	3,800	

Office Equipment		160
Bal.	22,500	

Accounts Payable		210
	8,000	Bal.

Unearned Revenue		215
	2,600	Bal.

Aaron Paquette, Capital		310
	9,500	Bal.

Aaron Paquette, Withdrawals		320
Bal.	2,000	

Consulting Revenues		410
	41,700	Bal.

Salaries Expense		510
Bal.	10,000	

Rent Expense		520
Bal.	7,500	

Utilities Expense		530
Bal.	1,000	

Name: _____

Exercise 2-11 (cont'd.)

Part 3

Trial Balance

Part 4

Income Statement

Exercise 2-11 (concl'd.)

Part 5

Statement of Changes in Equity		

Part 6

Balance Sheet			

Analysis component:

_____

_____

_____

_____

_____

_____

_____

_____

_____

_____

Exercise 2-12

GENERAL JOURNAL

Date	Account Titles and Explanation	PR	Debit	Credit
a.				
b.				
c.				
d.				
e.				
f.				
g.				

Exercise 2-13

GENERAL JOURNAL   Page____

Date		Account Titles and Explanation	PR	Debit	Credit

Exercise 2-14

GENERAL LEDGER

Cash   ACCOUNT NO. 101

DATE	EXPLANATION	PR	DEBIT	CREDIT	BALANCE
2022					
Dec. 31	Beginning balance				850

Accounts Receivable   ACCOUNT NO. 106

DATE	EXPLANATION	PR	DEBIT	CREDIT	BALANCE
2022					
Dec. 31	Beginning balance				300

Equipment   ACCOUNT NO. 167

DATE	EXPLANATION	PR	DEBIT	CREDIT	BALANCE
2022					
Dec. 31	Beginning balance				1,500

Accounts Payable   ACCOUNT NO. 201

DATE	EXPLANATION	PR	DEBIT	CREDIT	BALANCE
2022					
Dec. 31	Beginning balance				325

Toshi Sato, Capital   ACCOUNT NO. 301

DATE	EXPLANATION	PR	DEBIT	CREDIT	BALANCE
2022					
Dec. 31	Beginning balance				2,325

Exercise 2-14 (concl'd.)

Toshi Sato, Withdrawals   ACCOUNT NO. 302

DATE	EXPLANATION	PR	DEBIT	CREDIT	BALANCE
2022					
Dec. 31	Beginning balance				300

Revenue   ACCOUNT NO. 401

DATE	EXPLANATION	PR	DEBIT	CREDIT	BALANCE
2022					
Dec. 31	Beginning balance				1,800

Salaries Expense   ACCOUNT NO. 622

DATE	EXPLANATION	PR	DEBIT	CREDIT	BALANCE
2022					
Dec. 31	Beginning balance				1,500

Analysis component:

_____

_____

_____

_____

_____

_____

_____

_____

_____

_____

Exercise 2-15

GENERAL JOURNAL   Page____

Date	Account Titles and Explanation	PR	Debit	Credit

Name: _____

Exercise 2-16

Cash

ACCOUNT NO. 101

DATE	EXPLANATION	PR	DEBIT	CREDIT	BALANCE

Office Supplies

ACCOUNT NO. 124

DATE	EXPLANATION	PR	DEBIT	CREDIT	BALANCE

Prepaid Rent

ACCOUNT NO. 131

DATE	EXPLANATION	PR	DEBIT	CREDIT	BALANCE

Photography Equipment

ACCOUNT NO. 167

DATE	EXPLANATION	PR	DEBIT	CREDIT	BALANCE

Joseph Eagle, Capital

ACCOUNT NO. 301

DATE	EXPLANATION	PR	DEBIT	CREDIT	BALANCE

Photography Revenue

ACCOUNT NO. 401

DATE	EXPLANATION	PR	DEBIT	CREDIT	BALANCE

Utilities Expense

ACCOUNT NO. 690

DATE	EXPLANATION	PR	DEBIT	CREDIT	BALANCE

Exercise 2-16 (concl'd.)

Trial Balance	Debit	Credit

Analysis component:

_____
_____
_____
_____
_____
_____
_____
_____
_____
_____

Name: _____

Exercise 2-17

Cash 101	Office Supplies 124

	Photography Equipment 167

Prepaid Rent 131	Photography Revenue 401

Joseph Eagle, Capital 301	Utilities Expense 690

Trial Balance

	Debit	Credit

Analysis component:

_____
_____
_____
_____
_____
_____
_____
_____

Name: _____

Exercise 2-18

Income Statement

Statement of Changes in Equity

Balance Sheet

Analysis component:

_____

_____

_____

_____

_____

_____

_____

Income Statement

Statement of Changes in Equity

Balance Sheet

Exercise 2-20

Income Statement

Statement of Changes in Equity

Balance Sheet

Name: _____

Exercise 2-21

	Description	(1) Difference Between Debit and Credit Column	(2) Column With the Larger Total	(3) Identify Account(s) Incorrectly Stated	(4) Amount That Account(s) is Overstated or Understated
a.	A $2,400 debit to Rent Expense was posted as a $1,590 debit.	$810	Credit	Rent Expense	Rent Expense is understated by $810
b.	A $42,000 debit to Machinery was posted as a debit to Accounts Payable.				
c.	A $4,950 credit to Services Revenue was posted as a $495 credit.				
d.	A $1,440 debit to Store Supplies was not posted at all.				
e.	A $2,250 debit to Prepaid Insurance was posted as a debit to Insurance Expense.				
f.	A $4,050 credit to Cash was posted twice as two credits to the Cash account.				
g.	A $9,900 debit to the owner's withdrawals account was debited to the owner's capital account.				

Exercise 2-22

a. _____

_____

b. _____

_____

c. _____

_____

d. _____

_____

e. _____

_____

Exercise 2-23

Case A: _____
_____
_____
_____
_____
_____
_____
_____
_____
_____
_____

Case B: _____
_____
_____
_____
_____
_____
_____
_____
_____
_____
_____
_____
_____

Case C: _____
_____
_____
_____
_____
_____
_____
_____
_____
_____
_____
_____

Name: _____

Exercise 2-24

Income Statement

Exercise 2-25

Statement of Owner's Equity

Name: _____

Balance Sheet

Exercise 2-27

ERNST CONSULTING
Statement of Cash Flows
For Month Ended December 31, 2023

Problem 2-1A

Nov 1	Analysis				
	Journal entry analysis				
	Journal Entry				
	Date	**Account Titles and Explanation**		**Debit**	**Credit**
Nov 3	Analysis				
	Journal entry analysis				
	Journal Entry				
	Date	**Account Titles and Explanation**		**Debit**	**Credit**

Problem 2-1A (cont'd.)

Nov 7	Analysis	

	Journal entry analysis	

	Journal Entry			
	Date	**Account Titles and Explanation**	**Debit**	**Credit**

Nov 9	Analysis	

	Journal entry analysis	

	Journal Entry			
	Date	**Account Titles and Explanation**	**Debit**	**Credit**

Nov 13	Analysis	

	Journal entry analysis	

	Journal Entry			
	Date	**Account Titles and Explanation**	**Debit**	**Credit**

Name: _____

Problem 2-1A (cont'd.)

Nov 17	Analysis				
	Journal entry analysis				
	Journal Entry				
	Date	**Account Titles and Explanation**		**Debit**	**Credit**

Nov 21	Analysis				
	Journal entry analysis				
	Journal Entry				
	Date	**Account Titles and Explanation**		**Debit**	**Credit**

Nov 23	Analysis				
	Journal entry analysis				
	Journal Entry				
	Date	**Account Titles and Explanation**		**Debit**	**Credit**

Problem 2-1A (concl'd.)

Nov 27	Analysis				
	Journal entry analysis				
	Journal Entry				
	Date	**Account Titles and Explanation**		**Debit**	**Credit**
Nov 30	Analysis				
	Journal entry analysis				
	Journal Entry				
	Date	**Account Titles and Explanation**		**Debit**	**Credit**

Name: _____

Problem 2-2A Parts 1 and 2

Cash		Land

Accounts Receivable		Accounts Payable

		Long-Term Notes Payable

Accounts Receivable		Tobias Eaden, Capital

Supplies		Tobias Eaden, Withdrawals

Airplane		Revenue

Aircraft Equipment		Wages Expense

Building	

Name: _____

Problem 2-2A (concl'd.)
Part 3

_____
_____
_____
_____

Problem 2-3A

GENERAL JOURNAL

Page____

Date	Account Titles and Explanation	PR	Debit	Credit

Name: _____

Problem 2-3A (concl'd.)

GENERAL JOURNAL   Page____

Date	Account Titles and Explanation	PR	Debit	Credit

Problem 2-4A

GENERAL JOURNAL   Page____

Date	Account Titles and Explanation	PR	Debit	Credit

Problem 2-4A (concl'd.)

GENERAL JOURNAL   Page____

Date	Account Titles and Explanation	PR	Debit	Credit

Problem 2-5A   Parts 1 and 2

GENERAL LEDGER

Cash   ACCOUNT NO. 101

DATE	EXPLANATION	PR	DEBIT	CREDIT	BALANCE

Problem 2-5A (cont'd.)

Accounts Receivable — ACCOUNT NO. 106

DATE	EXPLANATION	PR	DEBIT	CREDIT	BALANCE

Office Supplies — ACCOUNT NO. 124

DATE	EXPLANATION	PR	DEBIT	CREDIT	BALANCE

Prepaid Insurance — ACCOUNT NO. 128

DATE	EXPLANATION	PR	DEBIT	CREDIT	BALANCE

Prepaid Rent — ACCOUNT NO. 131

DATE	EXPLANATION	PR	DEBIT	CREDIT	BALANCE

Office Equipment — ACCOUNT NO. 163

DATE	EXPLANATION	PR	DEBIT	CREDIT	BALANCE

Accounts Payable — ACCOUNT NO. 201

DATE	EXPLANATION	PR	DEBIT	CREDIT	BALANCE

Abe Factor, Capital — ACCOUNT NO. 301

DATE	EXPLANATION	PR	DEBIT	CREDIT	BALANCE

Abe Factor, Withdrawals — ACCOUNT NO. 302

DATE	EXPLANATION	PR	DEBIT	CREDIT	BALANCE

Problem 2-5A (concl'd.)

Accounting Revenue ACCOUNT NO. 401

DATE	EXPLANATION	PR	DEBIT	CREDIT	BALANCE

Utilities Expense ACCOUNT NO. 690

DATE	EXPLANATION	PR	DEBIT	CREDIT	BALANCE

Part 3

Trial Balance

Income Statement

Statement of Changes in Equity

Balance Sheet

Problem 2-7A

GENERAL JOURNAL

Date	Account Titles and Explanation	PR	Debit	Credit

Problem 2-7A (cont'd.)

GENERAL JOURNAL

Date	Account Titles and Explanation	PR	Debit	Credit

Chapter 2

Name: _____

Problem 2-7A (cont'd.)

Parts 2 and 3

GENERAL LEDGER

Cash — ACCOUNT NO. 101

DATE	EXPLANATION	PR	DEBIT	CREDIT	BALANCE

Accounts Receivable — ACCOUNT NO. 106

DATE	EXPLANATION	PR	DEBIT	CREDIT	BALANCE

Office Supplies — ACCOUNT NO. 124

DATE	EXPLANATION	PR	DEBIT	CREDIT	BALANCE

Prepaid Insurance — ACCOUNT NO. 128

DATE	EXPLANATION	PR	DEBIT	CREDIT	BALANCE

Prepaid Rent — ACCOUNT NO. 131

DATE	EXPLANATION	PR	DEBIT	CREDIT	BALANCE

Office Equipment — ACCOUNT NO. 163

DATE	EXPLANATION	PR	DEBIT	CREDIT	BALANCE

Problem 2-7A (cont'd.)

Accounts Payable — ACCOUNT NO. 201

DATE	EXPLANATION	PR	DEBIT	CREDIT	BALANCE

Elizabeth Wong, Capital — ACCOUNT NO. 301

DATE	EXPLANATION	PR	DEBIT	CREDIT	BALANCE

Elizabeth Wong, Withdrawals — ACCOUNT NO. 302

DATE	EXPLANATION	PR	DEBIT	CREDIT	BALANCE

Services Revenue — ACCOUNT NO. 403

DATE	EXPLANATION	PR	DEBIT	CREDIT	BALANCE

Wages Expense — ACCOUNT NO. 623

DATE	EXPLANATION	PR	DEBIT	CREDIT	BALANCE

Utilities Expense — ACCOUNT NO. 690

DATE	EXPLANATION	PR	DEBIT	CREDIT	BALANCE

Name: _____

Problem 2-7A (concl'd.)

Part 4

Trial Balance

Analysis component:

_____

_____

_____

_____

_____

_____

_____

_____

_____

_____

_____

Problem 2-8A

Income Statement

Statement of Changes in Equity

Balance Sheet

Problem 2-9A

Income Statement

Statement of Changes in Equity

Balance Sheet

Name: _____

Problem 2-9A (concl'd.)

Analysis component:

GENERAL JOURNAL

Page_____

Date		Account Titles and Explanation	PR	Debit	Credit

Problem 2-10A

Part 1

GENERAL JOURNAL

Page_____

Date		Account Titles and Explanation	PR	Debit	Credit

Problem 2-10A (cont'd.)

GENERAL JOURNAL

Page_____

Date		Account Titles and Explanation	PR	Debit	Credit

Problem 2-10A (cont'd.)

GENERAL JOURNAL   Page____

Date	Account Titles and Explanation	PR	Debit	Credit

Parts 2 and 3

GENERAL LEDGER

Cash   ACCOUNT NO. 101

DATE	EXPLANATION	PR	DEBIT	CREDIT	BALANCE
2023					
Jun. 30	Beginning balance				26,000

Problem 2-10A (cont'd.)

Accounts Receivable　　　　　　　　　　ACCOUNT NO. 106

DATE	EXPLANATION	PR	DEBIT	CREDIT	BALANCE
2023					
Jun. 30	Beginning balance				3,000

Prepaid Insurance　　　　　　　　　　ACCOUNT NO. 128

DATE	EXPLANATION	PR	DEBIT	CREDIT	BALANCE
2023					
Jun. 30	Beginning balance				500

Office Equipment　　　　　　　　　　ACCOUNT NO. 163

DATE	EXPLANATION	PR	DEBIT	CREDIT	BALANCE
2023					
Jun. 30	Beginning balance				1,700

Drafting Equipment　　　　　　　　　ACCOUNT NO. 167

DATE	EXPLANATION	PR	DEBIT	CREDIT	BALANCE
2023					
Jun. 30	Beginning balance				1,200

Building　　　　　　　　　　　　　　ACCOUNT NO. 173

DATE	EXPLANATION	PR	DEBIT	CREDIT	BALANCE
2023					
Jun. 30	Beginning balance				42,000

Land　　　　　　　　　　　　　　　ACCOUNT NO. 183

DATE	EXPLANATION	PR	DEBIT	CREDIT	BALANCE
2023					
Jun. 30	Beginning balance				28,000

Problem 2-10A (cont'd.)

Accounts Payable   ACCOUNT NO. 201

DATE	EXPLANATION	PR	DEBIT	CREDIT	BALANCE
2023					
Jun. 30	Beginning balance				1,740

Long-Term Notes Payable   ACCOUNT NO. 251

DATE	EXPLANATION	PR	DEBIT	CREDIT	BALANCE
2023					
Jun. 30	Beginning balance				24,000

Bob Binbutti, Capital   ACCOUNT NO. 301

DATE	EXPLANATION	PR	DEBIT	CREDIT	BALANCE
2023					
Jun. 30	Beginning balance				54,000

Bob Binbutti, Withdrawals   ACCOUNT NO. 302

DATE	EXPLANATION	PR	DEBIT	CREDIT	BALANCE
2023					
Jun. 30	Beginning balance				1,000

Engineering Revenue   ACCOUNT NO. 401

DATE	EXPLANATION	PR	DEBIT	CREDIT	BALANCE
2023					
Jun. 30	Beginning balance				29,600

Wages Expense   ACCOUNT NO. 623

DATE	EXPLANATION	PR	DEBIT	CREDIT	BALANCE
2023					
Jun. 30	Beginning balance				4,000

Problem 2-10A (concl'd.)

Equipment Rental Expense   ACCOUNT NO. 645

DATE	EXPLANATION	PR	DEBIT	CREDIT	BALANCE
2023					
Jun. 30	Beginning balance				1,000

Advertising Expense   ACCOUNT NO. 655

DATE	EXPLANATION	PR	DEBIT	CREDIT	BALANCE
2023					
Jun. 30	Beginning balance				640

Repairs Expense   ACCOUNT NO. 684

DATE	EXPLANATION	PR	DEBIT	CREDIT	BALANCE
2023					
Jun. 30	Beginning balance				300

Part 4

Trial Balance

Problem 2-11A

Income Statement

Statement of Changes in Equity

Balance Sheet

Name: _____

GENERAL JOURNAL

Page____

Date	Account Titles and Explanation	PR	Debit	Credit

Name: _____

Problem 2-12A (cont'd.)

Parts 2 and 3

Cash		101
Bal. 6,000		

Supplies		126
Bal. 950		

Equipment		161
Bal. 8,000		

Accounts Payable		201
	1,500	Bal.

Unearned Teaching Revenue		233
	9,800	Bal.

Teaching Revenue		401
	46,000	Bal.

Wages Expense		623
Bal. 26,350		

Taylor Smith, Capital		301
	3,000	Bal.

Rent Expense		640
Bal. 6,000		

Taylor Smith, Withdrawals		302
Bal. 13,000		

Name: _____

Problem 2-12A (cont'd)

Part 4

Trial Balance

Problem 2-12A (concl'd.)

Part 5

Income Statement

Statement of Changes in Equity

Balance Sheet

Name: _____

Problem 2-13A Part 1

GENERAL JOURNAL

Page____

Date	Account Titles and Explanation	PR	Debit	Credit

Problem 2-13A (cont'd.)

Parts 2 and 3

Cash		101
Bal.	6,200	

Supplies		126
Bal.	1,050	

Equipment		161
Bal.	8,200	

Accounts Payable		201
	1,700	Bal.

Wedding Planning Revenue		401
	46,600	Bal.

Unearned Wedding Planning Rev 233		
	10,000	Bal.

Wages Expense		623
Bal.	26,650	

Ranjeet Gill, Capital		301
	3,200	Bal.

Rent Expense		640
Bal.	6,200	

Ranjeet Gill, Withdrawals		302
Bal.	13,200	

Name: _____

Problem 2-13A (cont'd)

Part 4

Trial Balance		

Problem 2-13A (concl'd.)

Part 5

Income Statement

Statement of Changes in Equity

Balance Sheet

Income Statement

Statement of Changes in Equity

Balance Sheet

Name: _____

Problem 2-14A (concl'd)

Analysis component:

GENERAL JOURNAL

Page____

Date		Account Titles and Explanation	PR	Debit	Credit

Problem 2-15A

Trial Balance

Calculations:

Fundamental Accounting Principles, 17ce, Working Papers

Problem 2-1B

June 2	Analysis				
	Journal entry analysis				
	Journal Entry				
	Date	Account Titles and Explanation		Debit	Credit

Jun 4	Analysis				
	Journal entry analysis				
	Journal Entry				
	Date	Account Titles and Explanation		Debit	Credit

Jun 8	Analysis				
	Journal entry analysis				
	Journal Entry				
	Date	Account Titles and Explanation		Debit	Credit

Problem 2-1B (cont'd.)

Jun 10	Analysis				
	Journal entry analysis				
	Journal Entry				
	Date	Account Titles and Explanation		Debit	Credit

Jun 14	Analysis				
	Journal entry analysis				
	Journal Entry				
	Date	Account Titles and Explanation		Debit	Credit

Jun 18	Analysis				
	Journal entry analysis				
	Journal Entry				
	Date	Account Titles and Explanation		Debit	Credit

Chapter 2

Name: _____

Problem 2-1B (cont'd.)

Jun 22	Analysis	
	Journal entry analysis	
	Journal Entry	

Date	Account Titles and Explanations		Debit	Credit

Jun 24	Analysis	
	Journal entry analysis	
	Journal Entry	

Date	Account Titles and Explanations		Debit	Credit

Jun 28	Analysis	
	Journal entry analysis	
	Journal Entry	

Date	Account Titles and Explanations		Debit	Credit

Problem 2-1B (concl'd.)

Jun 30	Analysis				
	Journal entry analysis				
	Journal Entry				
	Date	**Account Titles and Explanations**		**Debit**	**Credit**

Name: _____

Problem 2-2B

Parts 1 and 2

Cash		Land

		Accounts Payable

		Long-Term Notes Payable

Accounts Receivable		Trevor Peters, Capital

Office Supplies		Trevor Peters, Withdrawals

Vehicle		Revenue

Office Equipment		Salaries Expense

Building		

Name: _____

Problem 2-2B (concl'd.)

Part 3

_____

_____

_____

_____

GENERAL JOURNAL
Page____

Date		Account Titles and Explanation	PR	Debit	Credit

Problem 2-3B (concl'd.)

GENERAL JOURNAL   Page____

Date	Account Titles and Explanation	PR	Debit	Credit

Problem 2-4B

GENERAL JOURNAL   Page____

Date	Account Titles and Explanation	PR	Debit	Credit

Problem 2-4B (concl'd.)

GENERAL JOURNAL

Page_____

Date	Account Titles and Explanation	PR	Debit	Credit

Name: _____

Problem 2-5B

Parts 1 and 2

GENERAL LEDGER

Cash   ACCOUNT NO. 101

DATE	EXPLANATION	PR	DEBIT	CREDIT	BALANCE

Accounts Receivable   ACCOUNT NO. 106

DATE	EXPLANATION	PR	DEBIT	CREDIT	BALANCE

Office Supplies   ACCOUNT NO. 124

DATE	EXPLANATION	PR	DEBIT	CREDIT	BALANCE

Prepaid Insurance   ACCOUNT NO. 128

DATE	EXPLANATION	PR	DEBIT	CREDIT	BALANCE

Prepaid Rent   ACCOUNT NO. 131

DATE	EXPLANATION	PR	DEBIT	CREDIT	BALANCE

Office Equipment   ACCOUNT NO. 163

DATE	EXPLANATION	PR	DEBIT	CREDIT	BALANCE

Problem 2-5B (cont'd.)

Accounts Payable   ACCOUNT NO. 201

DATE	EXPLANATION	PR	DEBIT	CREDIT	BALANCE

Francis Dhami, Capital   ACCOUNT NO. 301

DATE	EXPLANATION	PR	DEBIT	CREDIT	BALANCE

Francis Dhami, Withdrawals   ACCOUNT NO. 302

DATE	EXPLANATION	PR	DEBIT	CREDIT	BALANCE

Accounting Revenue   ACCOUNT NO. 401

DATE	EXPLANATION	PR	DEBIT	CREDIT	BALANCE

Professional Development Expense   ACCOUNT NO. 680

DATE	EXPLANATION	PR	DEBIT	CREDIT	BALANCE

Utilities Expense   ACCOUNT NO. 690

DATE	EXPLANATION	PR	DEBIT	CREDIT	BALANCE

Name: _____

Problem 2-5B (concl'd.)

Part 3

Trial Balance		

Income Statement

Statement of Changes in Equity

Balance Sheet

Problem 2-7B

Part 1

GENERAL JOURNAL

Page____

Date	Account Titles and Explanation	PR	Debit	Credit

Problem 2-7B (cont'd.)

GENERAL JOURNAL   Page____

Date		Account Titles and Explanation	PR	Debit	Credit

Parts 2 and 3

GENERAL LEDGER

Cash   ACCOUNT NO. 101

DATE	EXPLANATION	PR	DEBIT	CREDIT	BALANCE

Accounts Receivable   ACCOUNT NO. 106

DATE	EXPLANATION	PR	DEBIT	CREDIT	BALANCE

Problem 2-7B (cont'd.)

Office Supplies   ACCOUNT NO. 124

DATE	EXPLANATION	PR	DEBIT	CREDIT	BALANCE

Prepaid Insurance   ACCOUNT NO. 128

DATE	EXPLANATION	PR	DEBIT	CREDIT	BALANCE

Prepaid Rent   ACCOUNT NO. 131

DATE	EXPLANATION	PR	DEBIT	CREDIT	BALANCE

Office Equipment   ACCOUNT NO. 163

DATE	EXPLANATION	PR	DEBIT	CREDIT	BALANCE

Accounts Payable   ACCOUNT NO. 201

DATE	EXPLANATION	PR	DEBIT	CREDIT	BALANCE

Tait Unger, Capital   ACCOUNT NO. 301

DATE	EXPLANATION	PR	DEBIT	CREDIT	BALANCE

Tait Unger, Withdrawals   ACCOUNT NO. 302

DATE	EXPLANATION	PR	DEBIT	CREDIT	BALANCE

Problem 2-7B (concl'd.)

Service Revenue   ACCOUNT NO. 401

DATE	EXPLANATION	PR	DEBIT	CREDIT	BALANCE

Wages Expense   ACCOUNT NO. 680

DATE	EXPLANATION	PR	DEBIT	CREDIT	BALANCE

Utilities Expense   ACCOUNT NO. 690

DATE	EXPLANATION	PR	DEBIT	CREDIT	BALANCE

Part 4

Trial Balance

Analysis component:

_____

_____

_____

_____

_____

_____

Income Statement

Statement of Changes in Equity

Balance Sheet

Problem 2-9B

Income Statement

Statement of Changes in Equity

Balance Sheet

Name: _____

Problem 2-9B (concl'd.)

Analysis Component:

GENERAL JOURNAL   Page____

Date		Account Titles and Explanation	PR	Debit	Credit

Problem 2-10B   Part 1

GENERAL JOURNAL   Page____

Date		Account Titles and Explanation	PR	Debit	Credit

Name: _____

Problem 2-10B (cont'd.)

GENERAL JOURNAL

Page____

Date		Account Titles and Explanation	PR	Debit	Credit

Problem 2-10B (cont'd.)

Parts 2 and 3

GENERAL LEDGER

Cash — ACCOUNT NO. 101

DATE	EXPLANATION	PR	DEBIT	CREDIT	BALANCE
2023					
Jun. 30	Beginning balance				75,000

Accounts Receivable — ACCOUNT NO. 106

DATE	EXPLANATION	PR	DEBIT	CREDIT	BALANCE
2023					
Jun. 30	Beginning balance				950

Prepaid Insurance — ACCOUNT NO. 128

DATE	EXPLANATION	PR	DEBIT	CREDIT	BALANCE
2023					
Jun. 30	Beginning balance				275

Trucks — ACCOUNT NO. 153

DATE	EXPLANATION	PR	DEBIT	CREDIT	BALANCE
2023					
Jun. 30	Beginning balance				20,800

Problem 2-10B (cont'd.)

Office Equipment   ACCOUNT NO. 163

DATE	EXPLANATION	PR	DEBIT	CREDIT	BALANCE
2023					
Jun. 30	Beginning balance				1,200

Building   ACCOUNT NO. 173

DATE	EXPLANATION	PR	DEBIT	CREDIT	BALANCE
2023					
Jun. 30	Beginning balance				0

Land   ACCOUNT NO. 183

DATE	EXPLANATION	PR	DEBIT	CREDIT	BALANCE
2023					
Jun. 30	Beginning balance				0

Accounts Payable   ACCOUNT NO. 201

DATE	EXPLANATION	PR	DEBIT	CREDIT	BALANCE
2023					
Jun. 30	Beginning balance				725

Unearned Revenue   ACCOUNT NO. 233

DATE	EXPLANATION	PR	DEBIT	CREDIT	BALANCE
2023					
Jun. 30	Beginning balance				0

Long-Term Notes Payable   ACCOUNT NO. 251

DATE	EXPLANATION	PR	DEBIT	CREDIT	BALANCE
2023					
Jun. 30	Beginning balance				7,000

Problem 2-10B (cont'd.)

Brett Wilson, Capital   ACCOUNT NO. 301

DATE	EXPLANATION	PR	DEBIT	CREDIT	BALANCE
2023					
Jun. 30	Beginning balance				83,825

Brett Wilson, Withdrawals   ACCOUNT NO. 302

DATE	EXPLANATION	PR	DEBIT	CREDIT	BALANCE
2023					
Jun. 30	Beginning balance				600

Revenue   ACCOUNT NO. 401

DATE	EXPLANATION	PR	DEBIT	CREDIT	BALANCE
2023					
Jun. 30	Beginning balance				8,400

Wages Expense   ACCOUNT NO. 623

DATE	EXPLANATION	PR	DEBIT	CREDIT	BALANCE
2023					
Jun. 30	Beginning balance				780

Truck Rental Expense   ACCOUNT NO. 645

DATE	EXPLANATION	PR	DEBIT	CREDIT	BALANCE
2023					
Jun. 30	Beginning balance				230

Advertising Expense   ACCOUNT NO. 655

DATE	EXPLANATION	PR	DEBIT	CREDIT	BALANCE
2023					
Jun. 30	Beginning balance				75

Repairs Expense   ACCOUNT NO. 684

DATE	EXPLANATION	PR	DEBIT	CREDIT	BALANCE
2023					
Jun. 30	Beginning balance				40

Problem 2-10B (concl'd.)

Part 4

Trial Balance		

Name: _____

Income Statement

Statement of Changes in Equity

Balance Sheet

Problem 2-12B

Part 1

GENERAL JOURNAL

Date		Account Titles and Explanation	PR	Debit	Credit

Problem 2-12B (cont'd.)

Parts 2 and 3

Cash		101
Bal.	26,000	

Office Supplies		124
Bal.	900	

Office Equipment		163
Bal.	36,000	

Accounts Payable		201
	43,000	Bal.

Notes Payable		205
	20,000	Bal.

Ike Petrov, Capital		301
	8,000	Bal.

Ike Petrov, Withdrawals		302
Bal.	4,000	

Travel Revenue		401
	34,000	Bal.

Wages Expense		623
Bal.	38,000	

Interest Expense		633
Bal.	100	

Name: _____

Problem 2-12B (cont'd.)

Part 4

Trial Balance

Problem 2-12B (cont'd.)

Part 5

Income Statement

Statement of Changes in Equity

Balance Sheet

Name: _____

Problem 2-12B (concl'd.)

Analysis component:

_____
_____
_____
_____
_____
_____
_____
_____
_____

Name: _____

Problem 2-13B

Part 1

GENERAL JOURNAL

Page____

Date	Account Titles and Explanation	PR	Debit	Credit

Problem 2-13B (cont'd.)

Parts 2 and 3

Cash		101
Bal.	17,500	

Supplies		126
Bal.	1,700	

Equipment		161
Bal.	9,500	

Accounts Payable		201
	3,000	Bal.

Travel Planning Revenue		401
	60,500	Bal.

Unearned Travel Deposit Revenue		233
	11,300	Bal.

Wages Expense		623
Bal.	28,600	

Tom Keenan, Capital		301
	4,500	Bal.

Rent Expense		640
Bal.	7,500	

Tom Keenan, Withdrawals		302
Bal.	14,500	

Name: _____

Problem 2-13B (cont'd.)

Part 4

Trial Balance		

Income Statement

Problem 2-13B (concl'd.)

Statement of Changes in Equity

Balance Sheet

Problem 2-14B

Income Statement

Statement of Changes in Equity

Problem 2-14B (concl'd.)

Balance Sheet			

Analysis component: _____
_____
_____
_____
_____
_____
_____
_____

Name: _____

Problem 2-15B

	Trial Balance		

Calculations:

Name: _____

Cumulative Problem

Echo Systems

Parts 2 and 6: October/November Transactions

GENERAL JOURNAL

Date	Account Titles and Explanation	PR	Debit	Credit

Name: _____

Cumulative Problem

Echo Systems (Cont'd.)

Date		Account Titles and Explanation	PR	Debit	Credit

Name: _____

Cumulative Problem

Echo Systems (Cont'd.)

Date		Account Titles and Explanation	PR	Debit	Credit

Cumulative Problem (cont.)

Parts 1, 3, and 7   **GENERAL LEDGER**

Cash   ACCOUNT NO. 101

DATE	EXPLANATION	PR	DEBIT	CREDIT	BALANCE

Accounts Receivable   ACCOUNT NO. 106

DATE	EXPLANATION	PR	DEBIT	CREDIT	BALANCE

Computer Supplies   ACCOUNT NO. 126

DATE	EXPLANATION	PR	DEBIT	CREDIT	BALANCE

Cumulative Problem (cont'd.)

Prepaid Insurance   ACCOUNT NO. 128

DATE	EXPLANATION	PR	DEBIT	CREDIT	BALANCE

Prepaid Rent   ACCOUNT NO. 131

DATE	EXPLANATION	PR	DEBIT	CREDIT	BALANCE

Office Equipment   ACCOUNT NO. 163

DATE	EXPLANATION	PR	DEBIT	CREDIT	BALANCE

Computer Equipment   ACCOUNT NO. 167

DATE	EXPLANATION	PR	DEBIT	CREDIT	BALANCE

Accounts Payable   ACCOUNT NO. 201

DATE	EXPLANATION	PR	DEBIT	CREDIT	BALANCE

Mary Graham, Capital   ACCOUNT NO. 301

DATE	EXPLANATION	PR	DEBIT	CREDIT	BALANCE

Mary Graham, Withdrawals   ACCOUNT NO. 302

DATE	EXPLANATION	PR	DEBIT	CREDIT	BALANCE

Cumulative Problem (cont'd.)

Computer Services Revenue — ACCOUNT NO. 403

DATE	EXPLANATION	PR	DEBIT	CREDIT	BALANCE

Wages Expense — ACCOUNT NO. 623

DATE	EXPLANATION	PR	DEBIT	CREDIT	BALANCE

Advertising Expense — ACCOUNT NO. 655

DATE	EXPLANATION	PR	DEBIT	CREDIT	BALANCE

Mileage Expense — ACCOUNT NO. 676

DATE	EXPLANATION	PR	DEBIT	CREDIT	BALANCE

Repairs Expense, Computer — ACCOUNT NO. 684

DATE	EXPLANATION	PR	DEBIT	CREDIT	BALANCE

Charitable Donations Expense — ACCOUNT NO. 699

DATE	EXPLANATION	PR	DEBIT	CREDIT	BALANCE

Name: _____

Cumulative Problem (cont'd.)

Part 4

ECHO SYSTEMS		
Trial Balance		
October 31, 2023		
	Debit	**Credit**

Part 5

ECHO SYSTEMS		
Income Statement		
Month Ended October 31, 2023		

Fundamental Accounting Principles, 17ce, Working Papers

Cumulative Problem (cont'd.)

ECHO SYSTEMS

Statement of Changes in Equity

Month Ended October 31, 2023

ECHO SYSTEMS

Balance Sheet

October 31, 2023

Cumulative Problem (cont'd.)

Part 8

	Debit	Credit
ECHO SYSTEMS		
Trial Balance		
November 30, 2023		

Part 9

ECHO SYSTEMS		
Income Statement		
For Two Months Ended November 30, 2023		

Cumulative Problem (concl'd.)

ECHO SYSTEMS
Statement of Changes in Equity
For Two Months Ended November 30, 2023

ECHO SYSTEMS
Balance Sheet
November 30, 2023

Quick Study 3-1

Cash Accounting _____

_____

_____

_____

_____

Accrual Accounting _____

_____

_____

_____

_____

Quick Study 3-2

1. _____

_____

2. _____

_____

3. _____

_____

4. _____

_____

Quick Study 3-3

1. _____

_____

_____

_____

2. _____

_____

_____

_____

Fundamental Accounting Principles, 17ce, Working Papers

Quick Study 3-4

1. Cash Basis: _____
_____
_____
_____
_____

2. Accrual Basis: _____
_____
_____
_____

3. Difference: _____
_____
_____
_____
_____

Quick Study 3-5

a. _____
_____
_____

b. _____
_____
_____

GENERAL JOURNAL   Page____

Date	Account Titles and Explanation	Debit	Credit
c.			
d.			

Quick Study 3-6

a. _____
_____
_____

b. _____
_____
_____

GENERAL JOURNAL   Page____

Date	Account Titles and Explanation	Debit	Credit
c.			
d.			

Quick Study 3-7

GENERAL JOURNAL   Page____

Date	Account Titles and Explanation	Debit	Credit
a.			
b.			

c. _____
_____
_____

Quick Study 3-8

GENERAL JOURNAL   Page____

Date		Account Titles and Explanation	Debit	Credit
a.				

b. _____

_____

_____

GENERAL JOURNAL   Page____

Date		Account Titles and Explanation	Debit	Credit

c. _____

_____

_____

GENERAL JOURNAL   Page____

Date		Account Titles and Explanation	Debit	Credit

d. _____

_____

_____

_____

Name: _____

Quick Study 3-9

GENERAL JOURNAL

Page____

Date		Account Titles and Explanation	Debit	Credit
a.				

b. _____

_____

_____

GENERAL JOURNAL

Page____

Date		Account Titles and Explanation	Debit	Credit

c. _____

_____

_____

GENERAL JOURNAL

Page____

Date		Account Titles and Explanation	Debit	Credit

d. _____

_____

_____

_____

GENERAL JOURNAL

Page____

Date		Account Titles and Explanation	Debit	Credit
a.				

b. _____

_____

_____

GENERAL JOURNAL

Page____

Date		Account Titles and Explanation	Debit	Credit
c.				

d. _____

_____

_____

GENERAL JOURNAL

Page____

Date		Account Titles and Explanation	Debit	Credit
e.				

Quick Study 3-11

GENERAL JOURNAL   Page____

Date		Account Titles and Explanation	Debit	Credit
a.				

b. _____

_____

c. _____

_____

_____

GENERAL JOURNAL   Page____

Date		Account Titles and Explanation	Debit	Credit
d.				

Fundamental Accounting Principles, 17ce, Working Papers

Quick Study 3-12

GENERAL JOURNAL   Page____

Date		Account Titles and Explanation	Debit	Credit
a.				

b. _____

_____

_____

_____

GENERAL JOURNAL   Page____

Date		Account Titles and Explanation	Debit	Credit
c.				

d. _____

_____

_____

GENERAL JOURNAL   Page____

Date		Account Titles and Explanation	Debit	Credit
e.				

Quick Study 3-13

GENERAL JOURNAL   Page____

Date		Account Titles and Explanation	Debit	Credit
a.				

b. _____

_____

_____

_____

c. _____

_____

_____

_____

GENERAL JOURNAL   Page____

Date		Account Titles and Explanation	PR	Debit	Credit
d.					

Name: _____

GENERAL JOURNAL   Page____

Date		Account Titles and Explanation	PR	Debit	Credit
a.					

b. _____

_____

_____

_____

GENERAL JOURNAL   Page____

Date		Account Titles and Explanation	PR	Debit	Credit
c.					

Name: _____

Quick Study 3-15

a. _____
_____
_____

b. _____
_____
_____

GENERAL JOURNAL

Page____

Date		Account Titles and Explanation	PR	Debit	Credit
c.					

Quick Study 3-16

a. _____
_____
_____

GENERAL JOURNAL

Page____

Date		Account Titles and Explanation	PR	Debit	Credit
b.					

Fundamental Accounting Principles, 17ce, Working Papers

GENERAL JOURNAL   Page____

Date		Account Titles and Explanation	PR	Debit	Credit
a.					
b.					
c.					

Quick Study 3-18

a. _____

_____

_____

b. _____

_____

_____

GENERAL JOURNAL   Page____

Date		Account Titles and Explanation	PR	Debit	Credit
c.					
d.					

Name:_____

Quick Study 3-19

GENERAL JOURNAL   Page____

Date		Account Titles and Explanation	PR	Debit	Credit
a.					
b.					

Quick Study 3-20

GENERAL JOURNAL   Page____

Date		Account Titles and Explanation	PR	Debit	Credit
a.					
b.					

Quick Study 3-21

GENERAL JOURNAL   Page____

Date		Account Titles and Explanation	PR	Debit	Credit

Name: _____

a. _____
_____
_____
_____
_____
_____
_____
_____

GENERAL JOURNAL   Page____

Date	Account Titles and Explanation	PR	Debit	Credit
b.				
c.				

Quick Study 3-23

	Debits	Credits	
a.	_____	_____	Accrual of unpaid and unrecorded advertising that was used by Stark Company.
b.	_____	_____	Adjustment of Unearned Services Revenue to recognize earned revenue.
c.	_____	_____	Recorded revenue for work completed this accounting period; the cash will be received in the next period.
d.	_____	_____	The cost of Equipment was matched to the time periods benefited.
e.	_____	_____	Adjustment of Prepaid Advertising to recognize the portion used.

Quick Study 3-24

	Dr./Cr.	Account Titles	Statement
(a)	Debit		
	Credit		
(b)	Debit		
	Credit		
(c)	Debit		
	Credit		
(d)	Debit		
	Credit		
(e)	Debit		
	Credit		

Chapter 3   Name: _____

Quick Study 3-25

	Type of Adjustment	Profit will be overstated, understated, or no effect	Assets will be overstated, understated, or no effect	Liabilities will be overstated, understated, or no effect	Equity will be overstated, understated, or no effect
		If adjustment is not recorded:			
a.	Prepaid Expenses				
b.	Depreciation				
c.	Unearned Revenues				
d.	Accrued Expenses				
e.	Accrued Revenues				

Quick Study 3-26

GENERAL JOURNAL   Page____

Date	Account Titles and Explanation	PR	Debit	Credit

Name: _____

Income Statement

Statement of Owner's Equity

Balance Sheet

GENERAL JOURNAL

Page____

Date		Account Titles and Explanation	PR	Debit	Credit

Name: _____

*Quick Study 3-29

GENERAL JOURNAL

Page____

Date		Account Titles and Explanation	PR	Debit	Credit

*Quick Study 3-30

GENERAL JOURNAL

Page____

Date		Account Titles and Explanation	PR	Debit	Credit
a.					
b.					
c.					
d.					

Balance Sheet				Income Statement		
Prepaid Insurance				**Insurance Expense**		
	Accrual Basis*	Cash Basis			Accrual Basis**	Cash Basis
Dec. 31, Year 1......				Year 1.......		
Dec. 31, Year 2......				Year 2.......		
Dec. 31, Year 3......				Year 3.......		
Dec. 31, Year 4......				Year 4.......		
				Total.........		

Explanations:

_____
_____
_____
_____
_____
_____
_____
_____

Exercise 3-2

a.
_____
_____
_____

b.
_____
_____
_____

c.
_____
_____
_____
_____

Name: _____

Exercise 3-3

1.		7.	
2.		8.	
3.		9.	
4.		10.	
5.		11.	
6.		12.	

Exercise 3-4

GENERAL JOURNAL   Page____

Date	Account Titles and Explanation	PR	Debit	Credit
a.				

Exercise 3-4 (concl'd.)

Date		Account Titles and Explanation	PR	Debit	Credit
b.					
c.					

Exercise 3-5

Part 1: Calculations

a. _____

_____

_____

_____

b. _____

_____

_____

_____

c. _____

_____

_____

_____

_____

_____

Name: _____

Exercise 3-5 (concl'd.)

Part 1: Adjusting entries

GENERAL JOURNAL

Page_____

Date		Account Titles and Explanation	PR	Debit	Credit
a.					
b.					
c.					

2. _____

_____

_____

_____

3. _____

_____

_____

_____

Name: _____

GENERAL JOURNAL

Page____

Date		Account Titles and Explanation	PR	Debit	Credit
a.					
b.					
c.					

Name: _____

Exercise 3-7

GENERAL JOURNAL

Page____

	Date	Account Titles and Explanation	PR	Debit	Credit
a.					
b.					
c.					

Exercise 3-8

Part 1

GENERAL JOURNAL

Page____

	Date	Account Titles and Explanation	PR	Debit	Credit
a.					
b.					
c.					

Fundamental Accounting Principles, 17ce, Working Papers

Exercise 3-8 (concl'd.)

Date	Account Titles and Explanation	PR	Debit	Credit
d.				

Part 2

GENERAL JOURNAL   Page____

Date	Account Titles and Explanation	PR	Debit	Credit
a.				
b.				
c.				
d.				
e.				
f.				

Name: _____

Exercise 3-9

| | GENERAL JOURNAL | | | Page____ |

Date	Account Titles and Explanation	PR	Debit	Credit
a.				
b.				
c.				
d.				
e.				

Exercise 3-9 (concl'd.)

Date		Account Titles and Explanation	PR	Debit	Credit
f.					
g.					

Exercise 3-10

GENERAL JOURNAL   Page____

Date		Account Titles and Explanation	PR	Debit	Credit
1.					
2.					
a.					
b.					
c.					
d.					

Name: _____

Exercise 3-11

		GENERAL JOURNAL			Page____

Date		Account Titles and Explanation	PR	Debit	Credit
a.					
b.					
c.					
d.					
e.					
f.					

Fundamental Accounting Principles, 17ce, Working Papers

Exercise 3-12

GENERAL JOURNAL   Page____

Date	Account Titles and Explanation	PR	Debit	Credit
a.				
b.				
c.				

Exercise 3-13

GENERAL JOURNAL   Page____

Date	Account Titles and Explanation	PR	Debit	Credit
a.				
b.				
c.				
d.				
e.				

Exercise 3-14

a. _____
   _____
   _____
   _____

b. _____
   _____
   _____
   _____

c. _____
   _____
   _____
   _____

d. _____
   _____
   _____
   _____

Proof:

	(a)	(b)	(c)	(d)
Supplies on hand—January 1	$ 210	$ 810	$ 1,700	$____
Supplies purchased during the year	2,000	2,200		77,90
Total supplies available	$2,210	$3,010	$27,500	$93,30
Supplies on hand—December 31	(1,100)	____)	(2,400)	(8,20
Supplies expense for the year	$____	$ 750	$25,100	$85,10

Name: _____

Adjusting Entry:

GENERAL JOURNAL   Page____

Date		Account Titles and Explanation	PR	Debit	Credit

Payday Entry:

GENERAL JOURNAL   Page____

Date		Account Titles and Explanation	PR	Debit	Credit

Name: _____

Exercise 3-16

(a)
Adjusting Entry:

GENERAL JOURNAL   Page____

Date	Account Titles and Explanation	PR	Debit	Credit

Journal Entry (Next Period):

GENERAL JOURNAL   Page____

Date	Account Titles and Explanation	PR	Debit	Credit

(b)
Adjusting Entry:

GENERAL JOURNAL   Page____

Date	Account Titles and Explanation	PR	Debit	Credit

Journal Entry (Next Period):

GENERAL JOURNAL   Page____

Date	Account Titles and Explanation	PR	Debit	Credit

Exercise 3-16 (concl'd.)

(c)
Adjusting Entry:

GENERAL JOURNAL   Page____

Date	Account Titles and Explanation	PR	Debit	Credit

Journal Entry (Next Period):

GENERAL JOURNAL   Page____

Date	Account Titles and Explanation	PR	Debit	Credit

Exercise 3-17

GENERAL JOURNAL   Page____

Date	Account Titles and Explanation	PR	Debit	Credit

Exercise 3-17 (concl'd.)

<table>
<tr><th colspan="6">GENERAL JOURNAL   Page____</th></tr>
<tr><th>Date</th><th>Account Titles and Explanation</th><th>PR</th><th>Debit</th><th>Credit</th></tr>
<tr><td></td><td></td><td></td><td></td><td></td></tr>
<tr><td></td><td></td><td></td><td></td><td></td></tr>
<tr><td></td><td></td><td></td><td></td><td></td></tr>
<tr><td></td><td></td><td></td><td></td><td></td></tr>
<tr><td></td><td></td><td></td><td></td><td></td></tr>
<tr><td></td><td></td><td></td><td></td><td></td></tr>
<tr><td></td><td></td><td></td><td></td><td></td></tr>
<tr><td></td><td></td><td></td><td></td><td></td></tr>
<tr><td></td><td></td><td></td><td></td><td></td></tr>
<tr><td></td><td></td><td></td><td></td><td></td></tr>
<tr><td></td><td></td><td></td><td></td><td></td></tr>
<tr><td></td><td></td><td></td><td></td><td></td></tr>
<tr><td></td><td></td><td></td><td></td><td></td></tr>
<tr><td></td><td></td><td></td><td></td><td></td></tr>
<tr><td></td><td></td><td></td><td></td><td></td></tr>
<tr><td></td><td></td><td></td><td></td><td></td></tr>
<tr><td></td><td></td><td></td><td></td><td></td></tr>
<tr><td></td><td></td><td></td><td></td><td></td></tr>
<tr><td></td><td></td><td></td><td></td><td></td></tr>
<tr><td></td><td></td><td></td><td></td><td></td></tr>
<tr><td></td><td></td><td></td><td></td><td></td></tr>
<tr><td></td><td></td><td></td><td></td><td></td></tr>
</table>

Analysis component:
_____
_____
_____
_____
_____
_____
_____

Exercise 3-18

ACCOUNT	UNADJUSTED TRIAL BALANCE		ADJUSTMENTS		ADJUSTED TRIAL	
	Debit	Credit	Debit	Credit	Debit	Credit
Cash	$ 14,000					
Accounts receivable	32,000					
Prepaid insurance	16,800					
Equipment	102,000					
Accum. deprec., equipment		$ 23,000				
Accounts payable		19,000				
Abraham Nuna, capital		213,000				
Abraham Nuna, withdrawals	102,000					
Revenues		214,000				
Deprec. exp., equipment	-0-					
Salaries expense	187,700					
Insurance expense	14,500					
Totals	$469,000	$469,000				

Exercise 3-19

Income Statement		

Statement of Changes in Equity

Balance Sheet

Analysis component:

_____

_____

_____

_____

_____

Name: _____

*Exercise 3-20

GENERAL JOURNAL

Page____

Date		Account Titles and Explanation	PR	Debit	Credit
a.					
b.					

Name: _____

*Exercise 3-20 (concl'd.)

GENERAL JOURNAL

Page_____

Date		Account Titles and Explanation	PR	Debit	Credit
c.					
d.					

Analysis component:

_____
_____
_____
_____
_____
_____

*Exercise 3-21

GENERAL JOURNAL

Page____

Date		Account Titles and Explanation	PR	Debit	Credit
a.					
b.					
c.					
d.					
e.					
f.					

Name: _____

*Exercise 3-22

a. Initial credit recorded in Unearned Revenue account:

GENERAL JOURNAL   Page____

Date	Account Titles and Explanation	PR	Debit	Credit

Name: _____

*Exercise 3-22 (concl'd.)

b. Initial credit recorded in Revenue account:

GENERAL JOURNAL   Page____

Date		Account Titles and Explanation	PR	Debit	Credit

c.

_____
_____
_____
_____
_____
_____
_____
_____

Name: _____

Problem 3-1A

GENERAL JOURNAL

Page_____

Date		Account Titles and Explanation	PR	Debit	Credit
a.					
b.					
c.					
d.					

Analysis component:

_____
_____
_____
_____

Problem 3-2A

GENERAL JOURNAL

Page_____

Date		Account Titles and Explanation	PR	Debit	Credit
a.					
b.					
c.					

Problem 3-2A (concl'd.)

Analysis component:

_____
_____
_____
_____
_____
_____
_____
_____
_____

Problem 3-3A

GENERAL JOURNAL   Page____

Date	Account Titles and Explanation	PR	Debit	Credit
a.				
b.				
c.				
d.				

Analysis component:

_____
_____
_____
_____
_____
_____
_____
_____

Name: _____

Problem 3-4A

Adjusting Entries: GENERAL JOURNAL   Page____

Date	Account Titles and Explanation	PR	Debit	Credit
a.				
b.				
c.				
d.				
e.				

Name: _____

Problem 3-4A (concl'd.)

GENERAL JOURNAL Page____

Date	Account Titles and Explanation	PR	Debit	Credit
a.				
b.				
c.				
d.				
e.				

Name: _____

Problem 3-5A

Adjusting Entries: GENERAL JOURNAL Page____

Date	Account Titles and Explanation	PR	Debit	Credit
a.				
b.				
c.				
d.				

Subsequent Entries: GENERAL JOURNAL Page____

Date	Account Titles and Explanation	PR	Debit	Credit
a.				
b.				
c.				
d.				

Fundamental Accounting Principles, 17ce, Working Papers

Name: _____

Problem 3-6A

Part 1:

GENERAL JOURNAL

Page____

Date		Account Titles and Explanation	PR	Debit	Credit
a.					
b.					
c.					
d.					
e.					
f.					
g.					
h.					

Part 2: *See next page for Part 2 working paper.*

Part 3: _____
_____
_____

Part 4: _____
_____
_____
_____

Problem 3-6A (concl'd.)

Part 2

ACCOUNT	UNADJUSTED TRIAL BALANCE		ADJUSTMENTS		ADJUSTED TRIAL BALANCE	
	Debit	Credit	Debit	Credit	Debit	Credit
Cash	$ 18,000					
Accounts receivable	-0-					
Teaching supplies	6,500					
Prepaid insurance	1,400					
Prepaid rent	7,200					
Professional library	60,000					
Accum. deprec., professional library		18,000				
Equipment	96,000					
Accum. deprec., equipment		32,000				
Accounts payable		2,500				
Salaries payable		-0-				
Unearned extension revenue		6,300				
Karoo Ashevak, capital		229,000				
Karoo Ashevak, withdrawals	92,000					
Tuition revenue		196,000				
Extension revenue		72,500				
Deprec. exp., equipment	-0-					
Deprec. exp., prof library	-0-					
Salaries expense	206,000					
Insurance expense	-0-					
Rent expense	44,000					
Teaching supplies expense	-0-					
Advertising expense	14,000					
Utilities expense	11,200					
Totals	$556,300	$556,300				

Problem 3-7A

GENERAL JOURNAL   Page____

Date	Account Titles and Explanation	PR	Debit	Credit
a.				
b.				

Name: _____

Problem 3-7A (concl'd.)

GENERAL JOURNAL

Page____

Date		Account Titles and Explanation	PR	Debit	Credit
c.					
d.					
e.					
f.					
g.					
h.					
i.					
j.					

Name: _____

Problem 3-8A

Part 1   GENERAL JOURNAL   Page____

Date	Account Titles and Explanation	PR	Debit	Credit
a.				
b.				
c.				
d.				
e.				
f.				

Problem 3-8A (concl'd.)

Part 2   GENERAL JOURNAL   Page____

Date		Account Titles and Explanation	PR	Debit	Credit

Problem 3-9A

GENERAL JOURNAL   Page____

Date		Account Titles and Explanation	PR	Debit	Credit
a.					
b.					
c.					
d.					

Problem 3-9A (concl'd.)

GENERAL JOURNAL   Page____

Date	Account Titles and Explanation	PR	Debit	Credit
e.				
f.				
g.				
h.				
i.				

Problem 3-10A

Parts 1 and 2 (in balance column account format)

Note: The T-account template is provided at the end of this question.

GENERAL LEDGER

Cash   ACCOUNT NO. 101

DATE	EXPLANATION	PR	DEBIT	CREDIT	BALANCE
2023					
Oct. 31	Balance				26,000

Accounts Receivable   ACCOUNT NO. 106

DATE	EXPLANATION	PR	DEBIT	CREDIT	BALANCE
2023					
Oct. 31	Balance				61,000

Interest Receivable   ACCOUNT NO. 109

DATE	EXPLANATION	PR	DEBIT	CREDIT	BALANCE
2023					

Notes Receivable   ACCOUNT NO. 111

DATE	EXPLANATION	PR	DEBIT	CREDIT	BALANCE
2023					
Oct. 31	Balance				50,000

Supplies   ACCOUNT NO. 126

DATE	EXPLANATION	PR	DEBIT	CREDIT	BALANCE
2023					
Oct. 31	Balance				5,300

Prepaid Insurance   ACCOUNT NO. 128

DATE	EXPLANATION	PR	DEBIT	CREDIT	BALANCE
2023					
Oct. 31	Balance				3,400

Problem 3-10A (cont'd.)

Prepaid Rent   ACCOUNT NO. 131

DATE	EXPLANATION	PR	DEBIT	CREDIT	BALANCE
2023					
Oct. 31	Balance				27,000

Office Furniture   ACCOUNT NO. 161

DATE	EXPLANATION	PR	DEBIT	CREDIT	BALANCE
2023					
Oct. 31	Balance				84,000

Accumulated Depreciation, Office Furniture   ACCOUNT NO. 162

DATE	EXPLANATION	PR	DEBIT	CREDIT	BALANCE
2023					
Oct. 31	Balance				28,000

Accounts Payable   ACCOUNT NO. 201

DATE	EXPLANATION	PR	DEBIT	CREDIT	BALANCE
2023					
Oct. 31	Balance				18,000

Wages Payable   ACCOUNT NO. 210

DATE	EXPLANATION	PR	DEBIT	CREDIT	BALANCE
2023					

Unearned Consulting Revenue   ACCOUNT NO. 233

DATE	EXPLANATION	PR	DEBIT	CREDIT	BALANCE
2023					
Oct. 31	Balance				26,000

Jeff Moore, Capital   ACCOUNT NO. 301

DATE	EXPLANATION	PR	DEBIT	CREDIT	BALANCE
2023					
Oct. 31	Balance				223,000

Problem 3-10A (cont'd.)

Jeff Moore, Withdrawals   ACCOUNT NO. 302

DATE	EXPLANATION	PR	DEBIT	CREDIT	BALANCE
2023					
Oct. 31	Balance				28,000

Consulting Revenue   ACCOUNT NO. 401

DATE	EXPLANATION	PR	. DEBIT	CREDIT	BALANCE
2023					
Oct. 31	Balance				232,020

Interest Income   ACCOUNT NO. 409

DATE	EXPLANATION	PR	DEBIT	CREDIT	BALANCE
2023					
Oct. 31	Balance				480

Depreciation Expense, Office Furniture   ACCOUNT NO. 601

DATE	EXPLANATION	PR	DEBIT	CREDIT	BALANCE
2023					

Wages Expense   ACCOUNT NO. 622

DATE	EXPLANATION	PR	DEBIT	CREDIT	BALANCE
2023					
Oct. 31	Balance				192,000

Insurance Expense   ACCOUNT NO. 637

DATE	EXPLANATION	PR	DEBIT	CREDIT	BALANCE
2023					

Problem 3-10A (cont'd.)

Rent Expense   ACCOUNT NO. 640

DATE	EXPLANATION	PR	DEBIT	CREDIT	BALANCE
2023					
Oct. 31	Balance				44,000

Supplies Expense   ACCOUNT NO. 650

DATE	EXPLANATION	PR	DEBIT	CREDIT	BALANCE
2023					
Oct. 31	Balance				6,800

Adjusted Trial Balance

Part 4

Income Statement

Problem 3-10A (cont'd.)

Statement of Changes in Equity

Balance Sheet

Analysis component:

_____
_____
_____
_____
_____
_____

Problem 3-10A (cont'd.)

Part 1 and 2 (in T-account format)

Cash　101

Unadj Bal Oct 31　26,000	

Accounts Receivable　106

Unadj Bal Oct 31　61,000	

Interest Receivable　109

Notes Receivable　111

Unadj Bal Oct 31　50,000	

Supplies　126

Unadj Bal Oct 31　5,300	

Prepaid Insurance　128

Unadj Bal Oct 31　3,400	

Prepaid Rent　131

Unadj Bal Oct 31　27,000	

Office Furniture　161

Unadj Bal Oct 31　84,000	

Accum. Deprec., Office Furniture　162

	Unadj Bal Oct 31　28,000

Accounts Payable　201

	Unadj Bal Oct 31　18,000

Wages Payable　210

Unearned Consulting Revenue　233

	Unadj Bal Oct 31　26,000

Problem 3-10A (concl'd.)

Jeff Moore, Capital   301

		Unadj Bal Oct 31	223,000

Jeff Moore, Withdrawals   302

Unadj Bal Oct 31	28,000		

Consulting Revenue   401

		Unadj Bal Oct 31	232,020

Interest Income   409

		Unadj Bal Oct 31	480

Deprec. Expense, Office Furniture   601

Rent Expense   640

Unadj Bal Oct 31	44,000		

Insurance Expense   637

Wages Expense   622

Unadj Bal Oct 31	192,000		

Supplies Expense   650

Unadj Bal Oct 31	6,800		

GENERAL JOURNAL

Page____

Date		Account Titles and Explanation	PR	Debit	Credit
a.					
b.					
c.					
d.					
e.					
f.					
g.					

Name: _____

Problem 3-12A   Part 1

ACCOUNT	UNADJUSTED TRIAL BALANCE		ADJUSTMENTS		ADJUSTED TRIAL BALANCE	
	Debit	Credit	Debit	Credit	Debit	Credit
Cash	$ 6,000					
Accounts receivable	11,200					
Repair supplies	2,200					
Prepaid rent	14,000					
Office furniture	26,000					
Accounts payable		$ 8,000				
Notes payable		21,600				
Eli Arrow, capital		67,758				
Eli Arrow, withdrawals	5,000					
Hospitality revenues		128,000				
Salaries expense	144,000					
Wages expense	16,958					
Totals	$225,358	$225,358				

Part 2

Income Statement		

Problem 3-12A (concl'd.)

Statement of Changes in Equity

Balance Sheet

Analysis component:

_____
_____
_____
_____
_____
_____
_____
_____
_____

Name: _____

Problem 3-13A

Part 1

Income Statement		

Part 2

Statement of Changes in Equity		

Problem 3-13A (concl'd.)

Part 3

	Balance Sheet		

Analysis component:

_____

_____

_____

_____

_____

_____

_____

_____

_____

Name: _____

GENERAL JOURNAL

Page____

Date	Account Titles and Explanation	PR	Debit	Credit

Problem 3-14A (cont'd.)

Parts 2, 3 and 5

Cash	101

Prepaid Rent	131

Office Furniture	161

Accum. Deprec., Office Furn.	162

Accounts Payable	201

Unearned Revenue	233

Mark Diamond, Capital	301

Mark Diamond, Withdrawals	302

Revenue	401

Deprec. Exp., Office Furniture	602

Wages Expense	623

Rent Expense	640

Telephone Expense	688

Hotel Expenses	696

Problem 3-14A (cont'd.)

Part 4

Unadjusted Trial Balance

	Debit	Credit

Part 5 – Adjusting entries

GENERAL JOURNAL   Page____

Date		Account Titles and Explanation	PR	Debit	Credit

Problem 3-14A (cont'd.)

Part 6

Adjusted Trial Balance

	Debit	Credit

Part 7

Income Statement

Name: _____

Problem 3-14A (concl'd.)

Part 7 (concl'd.)

Statement of Changes in Equity

Balance Sheet

Analysis component:

_____

_____

_____

_____

_____

_____

_____

*Problem 3-15A

GENERAL JOURNAL   Page____

Date	Account Titles and Explanation	PR	Debit	Credit
a.				
b.				
c.				
d.				
e.				

Chapter 3

Name: _____

Analysis component:

_____
_____
_____
_____
_____
_____
_____
_____

Copyright © 2022 by McGraw Hill Ltd.

264

Fundamental Accounting Principles, 17ce, Working Papers

Name: _____

*Problem 3-16A

ACCOUNT	UNADJUSTED TRIAL BALANCE		ADJUSTMENTS		ADJUSTED TRIAL BALANCE	
	Debit	Credit	Debit	Credit	Debit	Credit
Cash	$ 32,000					
Accounts receivable	63,000					
Prepaid rent	-0-					
Prepaid insurance	-0-					
Accounts payable		$ 16,000				
Unearned consulting revenue		-0-				
Bruce Willis, capital		38,400				
Consulting revenue		82,000				
Rent expense	38,990					
Insurance expense	2,410					
Totals	$136,400	$136,400				

*Problem 3-17A

Part 1 - Entries that initially recognize assets and liabilities:

GENERAL JOURNAL

Page____

Date	Account Titles and Explanation	PR	Debit	Credit

*Problem 3-17A (cont'd.)

GENERAL JOURNAL   Page____

Date		Account Titles and Explanation	PR	Debit	Credit

Part 2 – Entries that initially recognize expenses and revenues:

GENERAL JOURNAL   Page____

Date		Account Titles and Explanation	PR	Debit	Credit

Name: _____

*Problem 3-17A (concl'd.)

Part 2 (concluded)

GENERAL JOURNAL

Page____

Date	Account Titles and Explanation	PR	Debit	Credit

Analysis component:

_____
_____
_____
_____
_____
_____
_____
_____
_____
_____
_____
_____
_____
_____
_____
_____
_____
_____
_____
_____

Name: _____

Problem 3-1B

GENERAL JOURNAL

Page____

Date		Account Titles and Explanation	PR	Debit	Credit
a.					
b.					
c.					
d.					

Analysis component:

_____
_____
_____
_____

Problem 3-2B

GENERAL JOURNAL

Page____

Date		Account Titles and Explanation	PR	Debit	Credit
a.					
b.					
c.					

Name: _____

Problem 3-2B (concl'd.)

Analysis component:

_____
_____
_____
_____
_____
_____
_____
_____
_____

Problem 3-3B

GENERAL JOURNAL

Page____

Date		Account Titles and Explanation	PR	Debit	Credit
a.					
b.					
c.					
d.					

Analysis component:

_____
_____
_____
_____
_____
_____
_____
_____

Name: _____

Problem 3-4B

Adjusting Entries:

GENERAL JOURNAL

Page_____

	Date	Account Titles and Explanation	PR	Debit	Credit
a.					
b.					
c.					
d.					
e.					

Problem 3-4B (concl'd.)

Subsequent Entries: **GENERAL JOURNAL**   Page____

Date	Account Titles and Explanation	PR	Debit	Credit
a.				
b.				
c.				
d.				
e.				

Name: _____

Problem 3-5B

Adjusting Entries: **GENERAL JOURNAL**   Page____

Date		Account Titles and Explanation	PR	Debit	Credit
a.					
b.					
c.					
d.					

Subsequent Entries: **GENERAL JOURNAL**   Page____

Date		Account Titles and Explanation	PR	Debit	Credit
a.					
b.					
c.					
d.					

Problem 3-6B
Part 1

GENERAL JOURNAL   Page____

Date	Account Titles and Explanation	PR	Debit	Credit
a.				
b.				
c.				
d.				
e.				
f.				
g.				
h.				

Part 2: *See next page for Part 2 working paper.*

Part 3: _____
_____
_____

Part 4: _____
_____
_____
_____

Problem 3-6B (concl'd.)

Part 2

ACCOUNT	UNADJUSTED TRIAL BALANCE		ADJUSTMENTS		ADJUSTED TRIAL	
	Debit	Credit	Debit	Credit	Debit	Credit
Cash	$ 25,000					
Accounts receivable	-0-					
Teaching supplies	107,200					
Prepaid insurance	36,000					
Prepaid rent	11,600					
Professional library	20,000					
Accum. deprec., professional library		3,000				
Equipment	141,400					
Accum. deprec., equipment		32,000				
Accounts payable		24,400				
Salaries payable		-0-				
Unearned extension revenue		55,200				
Jay Fawcett, capital		62,000				
Jay Fawcett, withdrawals	40,000					
Tuition revenue		285,000				
Extension revenue		124,000				
Deprec. exp., equipment	-0-					
Deprec. exp., profl library	-0-					
Salaries expense	143,600					
Insurance expense	-0-					
Rent expense	-0-					
Teaching supplies expense	-0-					
Advertising expense	36,000					
Utilities expense	24,800					
Totals	$585,600	$585,600				

Problem 3-7B

Adjusting Entries: **GENERAL JOURNAL** Page____

Date		Account Titles and Explanation	PR	Debit	Credit
a.					
b.					

Name: _____

Problem 3-7B (concl'd.)

GENERAL JOURNAL Page____

Date		Account Titles and Explanation	PR	Debit	Credit
c.					
d.					
e.					
f.					
g.					
h.					
i.					
j.					

Problem 3-8B

Part 1   GENERAL JOURNAL   Page____

Date		Account Titles and Explanation	PR	Debit	Credit
a.					
b.					
c.					
d.					
e.					
f.					

Problem 3-8B (concl'd.)

Part 2   GENERAL JOURNAL   Page____

Date	Account Titles and Explanation	PR	Debit	Credit

Problem 3-9B

GENERAL JOURNAL   Page____

Date	Account Titles and Explanation	PR	Debit	Credit
a.				
b.				
c.				
d.				

Problem 3-9B (concl'd.)

GENERAL JOURNAL   Page____

Date		Account Titles and Explanation	PR	Debit	Credit
e.					
f.					
g.					
h.					
i.					

Analysis component:

_____

_____

_____

_____

_____

_____

_____

_____

Name: _____

Problem 3-10B

Parts 1 and 2

Cash   ACCOUNT NO. 101

DATE	EXPLANATION	PR	DEBIT	CREDIT	BALANCE
2023					
Dec. 31	Balance				15,600

Accounts Receivable   ACCOUNT NO. 106

DATE	EXPLANATION	PR	DEBIT	CREDIT	BALANCE
2023					
Dec. 31	Balance				29,200

Supplies   ACCOUNT NO. 126

DATE	EXPLANATION	PR	DEBIT	CREDIT	BALANCE
2023					
Dec. 31	Balance				1,640

Prepaid Advertising   ACCOUNT NO. 128

DATE	EXPLANATION	PR	DEBIT	CREDIT	BALANCE
2023					
Dec. 31	Balance				1,280

Prepaid Rent   ACCOUNT NO. 131

DATE	EXPLANATION	PR	DEBIT	CREDIT	BALANCE
2023					
Dec. 31	Balance				17,880

Surveying Equipment   ACCOUNT NO. 167

DATE	EXPLANATION	PR	DEBIT	CREDIT	BALANCE
2023					
Dec. 31	Balance				58,000

Accum. Deprec. – Surveying Equipment   ACCOUNT NO. 168

DATE	EXPLANATION	PR	DEBIT	CREDIT	BALANCE
2023					
Dec. 31	Balance				7,348

Problem 3-10B (cont'd.)

Accounts Payable — ACCOUNT NO. 201

DATE	EXPLANATION	PR	DEBIT	CREDIT	BALANCE
2023					
Dec. 31	Balance				13,800

Interest Payable — ACCOUNT NO. 203

DATE	EXPLANATION	PR	DEBIT	CREDIT	BALANCE
2023					

Wages Payable — ACCOUNT NO. 210

DATE	EXPLANATION	PR	DEBIT	CREDIT	BALANCE
2023					

Unearned Surveying Revenue — ACCOUNT NO. 233

DATE	EXPLANATION	PR	DEBIT	CREDIT	BALANCE
2023					
Dec. 31	Balance				14,800

Notes Payable — ACCOUNT NO. 251

DATE	EXPLANATION	PR	DEBIT	CREDIT	BALANCE
2023					
Dec. 31	Balance				36,000

Ben Hallmark, Capital — ACCOUNT NO. 301

DATE	EXPLANATION	PR	DEBIT	CREDIT	BALANCE
2023					
Dec. 31	Balance				28,652

Ben Hallmark, Withdrawals — ACCOUNT NO. 302

DATE	EXPLANATION	PR	DEBIT	CREDIT	BALANCE
2023					
Dec. 31	Balance				24,300

Problem 3-10B (cont'd.)

Surveying Revenue   ACCOUNT NO. 401

DATE	EXPLANATION	PR	DEBIT	CREDIT	BALANCE
2023					
Dec. 31	Balance				170,948

Depreciation Expense, Surveying Equipment   ACCOUNT NO. 601

DATE	EXPLANATION	PR	DEBIT	CREDIT	BALANCE
2023					

Salaries Expense   ACCOUNT NO. 622

DATE	EXPLANATION	PR	DEBIT	CREDIT	BALANCE
2023					
Dec. 31	Balance				56,000

Wages Expense   ACCOUNT NO. 623

DATE	EXPLANATION	PR	DEBIT	CREDIT	BALANCE
2023					
Dec. 31	Balance				39,726

Interest Expense   ACCOUNT NO. 633

DATE	EXPLANATION	PR	DEBIT	CREDIT	BALANCE
2023					

Insurance Expense   ACCOUNT NO. 637

DATE	EXPLANATION	PR	DEBIT	CREDIT	BALANCE
2023					
Dec. 31	Balance				6,000

Rent Expense   ACCOUNT NO. 640

DATE	EXPLANATION	PR	DEBIT	CREDIT	BALANCE
2023					

Problem 3-10B (cont'd.)

Supplies Expense   ACCOUNT NO. 650

DATE	EXPLANATION	PR	DEBIT	CREDIT	BALANCE
2023					
Dec. 31	Balance				2,958

Advertising Expense   ACCOUNT NO. 655

DATE	EXPLANATION	PR	DEBIT	CREDIT	BALANCE
2023					

Gas and Oil Expense   ACCOUNT NO. 671

DATE	EXPLANATION	PR	DEBIT	CREDIT	BALANCE
2023					
Dec. 31	Balance				6,564

Repairs Expense   ACCOUNT NO. 684

DATE	EXPLANATION	PR	DEBIT	CREDIT	BALANCE
2023					
Dec. 31	Balance				12,400

Utilities Expense   ACCOUNT NO. 690

DATE	EXPLANATION	PR	DEBIT	CREDIT	BALANCE
2023					

Problem 3-10B (cont'd.) Part 3

Adjusted Trial Balance

Problem 3-10B (cont'd.) Part 4

Income Statement

Statement of Changes in Equity

Name: _____

Problem 3-10B (concl'd.)

Balance Sheet		

Analysis component:

_____
_____
_____
_____
_____
_____
_____
_____
_____
_____

Name: _____

Problem 3-11B

GENERAL JOURNAL

Page____

Date	Account Titles and Explanation	PR	Debit	Credit
a.				
b.				
c.				
d.				
e.				
f.				
g.				

Problem 3-12B Part 1

ACCOUNT	UNADJUSTED TRIAL BALANCE		ADJUSTMENT		ADJUSTED TRIAL	
	Debit	Credit	Debit	Credit	Debit	Credit
Cash	$ 112,000					
Accounts receivable	28,000					
Repair supplies	2,800					
Prepaid arena rental	182,000					
Skate equipment	428,000					
Accum. deprec., skate eq.		$ 164,000				
Accounts payable		5,400				
Unearned training revenue		19,600				
Notes payable		160,000				
Ben Gibson, capital		451,400				
Ben Gibson, withdrawals	72,000					
Training revenue		550,000				
Salaries expense	350,000					
Arena rental expense	168,000					
Other expenses	7,600					
Totals	$1,350,400	$1,350,400				

Part 2

Income Statement

Problem 3-12B (concl'd.)

Statement of Changes in Equity

Balance Sheet

Analysis component:

Fundamental Accounting Principles, 17ce, Working Papers

Name: _____

Problem 3-13B

Part 1

Income Statement		

Part 2

Statement of Changes in Equity		

Name: _____

Problem 3-13B (concl'd.)

Part 3

Balance Sheet		

Chapter 3

Problem 3-14B   Part 1

Page____

Date	Account Titles and Explanation	PR	Debit	Credit

Copyright © 2022 by McGraw Hill Ltd.
Fundamental Accounting Principles, 17ce, Working Papers   291

Problem 3-14B (cont'd.)

Parts 2, 3, and 5

Cash			101
Bal.	6,400		

Repair Supplies			131
Bal.	3,000		

Accum. Deprec., Tools			162
		560	Bal.

Tools			161
Bal.	16,800		

Unearned Revenue			233
		700	Bal.

Accounts Payable			201
		3,200	Bal.

Melanie Thornhill, Capital			301
			Bal.

Melanie Thornhill, Withdrawals			302
Bal.	-0-		

Revenue			401
		25,800	Bal.

Deprec. Exp., Tools			602
Bal.	560		

Wages Expense			623
Bal.	1,960		

Rent Expense			640
Bal.	8,000		

Repair Supplies Expense			696
Bal.	2,700		

Problem 3-14B (cont'd.)

Part 4

Unadjusted Trial Balance

	Debit	Credit

Part 5 – Adjusting entries

GENERAL JOURNAL

Page____

Date	Account Titles and Explanation	PR	Debit	Credit

Name: _____

Problem 3-14B (cont'd.)

Part 6

Adjusted Trial Balance	Debit	Credit

Part 7

Income Statement		

Fundamental Accounting Principles, 17ce, Working Papers

Problem 3-14B (concl'd.)

Part 6 (concl'd.)

Statement of Changes in Equity

Balance Sheet

Analysis component:

_____

_____

_____

_____

_____

_____

_____

_____

Name: _____

*Problem 3-15B

| | GENERAL JOURNAL | | | Page____ |

Date	Account Titles and Explanation	PR	Debit	Credit
a.				
b.				
c.				
d.				
e.				

Analysis component:

_____
_____
_____
_____
_____
_____
_____
_____

Name: _____

*Problem 3-16B

ACCOUNT	UNADJUSTED TRIAL BALANCE		ADJUSTMENTS		ADJUSTED TRIAL	
	Debit	Credit	Debit	Credit	Debit	Credit
Cash	$ 3,500					
Accounts receivable	7,200					
Prepaid advertising	-0-					
Cleaning supplies	-0-					
Equipment	29,000					
Accum. deprec., equipment		$ 3,200				
Unearned window washing revenue		-0-				
Unearned office cleaning revenue		-0-				
William Nahanee, capital		9,150				
Window washing fees revenue		23,800				
Office cleaning fees revenue		71,500				
Advertising expense	2,900					
Salaries expense	56,900					
Depreciation expense, equip.	-0-					
Cleaning supplies expense	8,150					
Totals	$107,650	$107,650				

*Problem 3-17B

Part 1 - Entries that initially recognize assets and liabilities:

GENERAL JOURNAL   Page____

Date	Account Titles and Explanation	PR	Debit	Credit

Name: _____

*Problem 3-17B (cont'd.)

GENERAL JOURNAL

Page_____

Date	Account Titles and Explanation	PR	Debit	Credit

Part 2 – Entries that initially recognize expenses and revenues:

GENERAL JOURNAL

Page_____

Date	Account Titles and Explanation	PR	Debit	Credit

Name: _____

*Problem 3-17B (concl'd.)

Part 2 (concl'd)

GENERAL JOURNAL

Page____

Date		Account Titles and Explanation	PR	Debit	Credit

Analysis component:

_____
_____
_____
_____
_____
_____
_____
_____
_____
_____
_____
_____
_____
_____
_____
_____

Cumulative Problem

Part 1   **Echo Systems**
             Journal Entries

GENERAL JOURNAL

Page____

Date	Account Titles and Explanation	PR	Debit	Credit

Name: _____

Cumulative Problem

Part 2　　　**Echo Systems**
　　　　　　　　Adjusting Entries

GENERAL JOURNAL

Page____

Date	Account Titles and Explanation	PR	Debit	Credit

Cumulative Problem

Part 2   Echo Systems (Cont'd.)

GENERAL LEDGER

Cash   ACCOUNT NO. 101

DATE	EXPLANATION	PR	DEBIT	CREDIT	BALANCE
2023 Nov. 30	Balance				70,340

Accounts Receivable   ACCOUNT NO. 106

DATE	EXPLANATION	PR	DEBIT	CREDIT	BALANCE
2023 Nov. 30	Balance				18,900

Computer Supplies   ACCOUNT NO. 126

DATE	EXPLANATION	PR	DEBIT	CREDIT	BALANCE
2023 Nov. 30	Balance				4,560

Prepaid Insurance   ACCOUNT NO. 128

DATE	EXPLANATION	PR	DEBIT	CREDIT	BALANCE
2023 Nov. 30	Balance				4,320

Prepaid Rent   ACCOUNT NO. 131

DATE	EXPLANATION	PR	DEBIT	CREDIT	BALANCE
2023 Nov. 30	Balance				9,000

Cumulative Problem

Part 2   **Echo Systems (Cont'd.)**

Office Equipment   ACCOUNT NO. 163

DATE	EXPLANATION	PR	DEBIT	CREDIT	BALANCE
2023 Nov. 30	Balance				18,000

Accumulated Depreciation, Office Equipment   ACCOUNT NO. 164

DATE	EXPLANATION	PR	DEBIT	CREDIT	BALANCE
2023 Nov. 30	Balance				-0-

Computer Equipment   ACCOUNT NO. 167

DATE	EXPLANATION	PR	DEBIT	CREDIT	BALANCE
2023 Nov. 30	Balance				36,000

Accumulated Depreciation, Computer Equipment   ACCOUNT NO. 168

DATE	EXPLANATION	PR	DEBIT	CREDIT	BALANCE
2023 Nov. 30	Balance				-0-

Accounts Payable   ACCOUNT NO. 201

DATE	EXPLANATION	PR	DEBIT	CREDIT	BALANCE
2023 Nov. 30	Balance				-0-

Wages Payable   ACCOUNT NO. 210

DATE	EXPLANATION	PR	DEBIT	CREDIT	BALANCE
2023 Nov. 30	Balance				-0-

Unearned Computer Services Revenue   ACCOUNT NO. 236

DATE	EXPLANATION	PR	DEBIT	CREDIT	BALANCE
2023 Nov. 30	Balance				-0-

Mary Graham, Capital   ACCOUNT NO. 301

DATE	EXPLANATION	PR	DEBIT	CREDIT	BALANCE
2023 Nov. 30	Balance				144,000

Cumulative Problem

Part 2   **Echo Systems (Cont'd.)**

Mary Graham, Withdrawals   ACCOUNT NO. 302

DATE	EXPLANATION	PR	DEBIT	CREDIT	BALANCE
2023 Nov. 30	Balance				10,800

Computer Services Revenue   ACCOUNT NO. 403

DATE	EXPLANATION	PR	DEBIT	CREDIT	BALANCE
2023 Nov. 30	Balance				40,950

Depreciation Expense, Office Equipment   ACCOUNT NO. 612

DATE	EXPLANATION	PR	DEBIT	CREDIT	BALANCE
2023 Nov. 30	Balance				-0-

Depreciation Expense, Computer Equipment   ACCOUNT NO. 613

DATE	EXPLANATION	PR	DEBIT	CREDIT	BALANCE
2023 Nov. 30	Balance				-0-

Wages Expense   ACCOUNT NO. 623

DATE	EXPLANATION	PR	DEBIT	CREDIT	BALANCE
2023 Nov. 30	Balance				4,200

Insurance Expense   ACCOUNT NO. 637

DATE	EXPLANATION	PR	DEBIT	CREDIT	BALANCE
2023 Nov. 30	Balance				-0-

Rent Expense   ACCOUNT NO. 640

DATE	EXPLANATION	PR	DEBIT	CREDIT	BALANCE
2023 Nov. 30	Balance				-0-

Chapter 3   Name: _____

Cumulative Problem

Part 2   Echo Systems (Cont'd.)

Computer Supplies Expense — ACCOUNT NO. 652

DATE	EXPLANATION	PR	DEBIT	CREDIT	BALANCE
2023 Nov. 30	Balance				-0-

Advertising Expense — ACCOUNT NO. 655

DATE	EXPLANATION	PR	DEBIT	CREDIT	BALANCE
2023 Nov. 30	Balance				3,720

Mileage Expense — ACCOUNT NO. 676

DATE	EXPLANATION	PR	DEBIT	CREDIT	BALANCE
2023 Nov. 30	Balance				2,200

Repairs Expense, Computer — ACCOUNT NO. 684

DATE	EXPLANATION	PR	DEBIT	CREDIT	BALANCE
2023 Nov. 30	Balance				1,410

Charitable Donations Expense — ACCOUNT NO. 699

DATE	EXPLANATION	PR	DEBIT	CREDIT	BALANCE
2023 Nov. 30	Balance				1,500

Cumulative Problem

Part 3　　　　Echo Systems (Cont'd.)

ECHO SYSTEMS
Adjusted Trial Balance
December 31, 2023

	Debit	Credit

Cumulative Problem

Part 4   Echo Systems (Cont'd.)

ECHO SYSTEMS
Income Statement
For Three Months Ended December 31, 2023

ECHO SYSTEMS
Statement of Changes in Equity
For Three Months Ended December 31, 2023

Cumulative Problem

Part 5   Echo Systems (Concl'd.)

ECHO SYSTEMS
Balance Sheet
December 31, 2023

Quick Study 4-1

1. _____
   _____
   _____
   _____

2. _____
   _____
   _____
   _____

3. _____
   _____
   _____

4. _____
   _____
   _____
   _____

Quick Study 4-2

Account	(1) Temporary?	(1) Permanent?	(2) Financial Statement?
a. Accounts Payable			
b. Insurance Expense			
c. Delivery Vehicle			
d. Interest Income			
e. Unearned Revenue			
f. Accumulated Depreciation			
g. Stephos Petridis, Capital			
h. Depreciation Expense			
i. Stephos Petridis, withdrawals			
j. Wages Payable			
k. Prepaid Insurance			
l. Utility Expense			
m. Building			
n. Supplies Expense			

Name: _____

Quick Study 4-3

a. _____

_____

_____

_____

_____

_____

b. _____

_____

_____

_____

_____

_____

Chapter 4

Quick Study 4-4

Name: _____

GENERAL JOURNAL

Page____

Date	Account Titles and Explanation	PR	Debit	Credit

Assets

250

Capital

200

Revenue

100

Liabilities

30

Withdrawals

20

Expenses

60

Income Summary

Name: _____

Quick Study 4-5

GENERAL JOURNAL

Page____

Date	Account Titles and Explanation	PR	Debit	Credit

Assets

250

Capital

200

Revenue

100

Liabilities

110

Withdrawals

20

Expenses

140

Income Summary

Quick Study 4-6

Post-Closing Trial Balance		
	Debit	**Credit**

Quick Study 4-7

a. _____ Preparing the unadjusted trial balance.
b. _____ Preparing the post-closing trial balance.
c. _____ Journalizing and posting adjusting entries.
d. _____ Journalizing and posting closing entries.
e. _____ Preparing the financial statements.
f. _____ Journalizing transactions.
g. _____ Posting the transaction entries.
h. _____ Completing the work sheet.

Quick Study 4-8

1. _____ Store equipment
2. _____ Wages payable
3. _____ Cash
4. _____ Notes payable (due in three years)
5. _____ Land not currently used in business operations
6. _____ Accounts receivable
7. _____ Trademarks

Quick Study 4-9

1. _____	Depreciation expense, trucks	11. _____	Accum. deprec., trucks
2. _____	Lee Hale, capital	12. _____	Cash
3. _____	Interest receivable	13. _____	Building
4. _____	Lee Hale, withdrawals	14. _____	Brand name
5. _____	Automobiles	15. _____	Office equipment
6. _____	Notes payable (due in 3 years)	16. _____	Land (used in operations)
7. _____	Accounts payable	17. _____	Repairs expense
8. _____	Prepaid insurance	18. _____	Prepaid property taxes
9. _____	Land not currently used in business operations	19. _____	Notes payable (due in 2 months)
10. _____	Unearned services revenue	20. _____	Notes receivable (due in 2 years)

Quick Study 4-10

Partial Balance Sheet

Quick Study 4-11

Name: _____

Quick Study 4-12

_____
_____
_____
_____
_____
_____
_____
_____
_____
_____

Quick Study 4-13

	2020	2019
Debt to equity ratio		

Comments: _____
_____
_____
_____
_____

*Quick Study 4-14

1. _____ Equipment
2. _____ Owner, withdrawals
3. _____ Insurance expense

4. _____ Prepaid insurance
5. _____ Accounts receivable
6. _____ Depreciation expense, equipment

*Quick Study 4-15

-see next page for *QS 4-15 working paper

*Quick Study 4-16

_____
_____
_____
_____
_____
_____
_____
_____
_____
_____
_____

*Quick Study 4-17

_____
_____
_____
_____
_____
_____
_____
_____
_____
_____
_____
_____
_____
_____
_____
_____
_____
_____

*Fundamental Accounting Principles,*17ce, Working Papers

Name: _____

***Quick Study 4-15**

Account Title	Unadjusted Trial Balance		Adjustments		Adjusted Trial Balance		Income Statement		Balance Sheet & Statement of Changes in Equity	
	Debit	Credit	Debit	Credit	Debit	Credit	Debit	Credit	Debit	Credit
Cash	15									
Accounts receivable	22									
Supplies	25			8						
Ed Wolt, capital		40								
Ed Wolt, withdrawals	12									
Service Revenue		48								
Supplies expense	14	—	8	—						
Totals	88	88	8	8						

Exercise 4-1

GENERAL JOURNAL

Page____

Date	Account Titles and Explanation	PR	Debit	Credit

Post-Closing Trial Balance

	Debit	Credit

Exercise 4-2

GENERAL JOURNAL   Page____

Date	Account Titles and Explanation	PR	Debit	Credit

Exercise 4-3

Part 1

Adjusted Trial Balance

	Debit	Credit

Name: _____

Exercise 4-3 (concl'd.)

Explanation: _____
_____
_____
_____
_____
_____

Part 2. Closing entries:

GENERAL JOURNAL   Page____

Date	Account Titles and Explanation	PR	Debit	Credit

Part 3.

Nick Stilz, Capital

GENERAL JOURNAL

Page____

Date		Account Titles and Explanation	PR	Debit	Credit

Post-Closing Trial Balance

	Debit	Credit

Exercise 4-5

Income Statement

Statement of Changes in Equity

Balance Sheet			

K. Wilson, Capital is computed as follows:

Exercise 4-7

GENERAL JOURNAL

Page____

Date	Account Titles and Explanation	PR	Debit	Credit

Exercise 4-8

GENERAL JOURNAL

Date		Account Titles and Explanation	PR	Debit	Credit

Exercise 4-8 (concl'd.)

Posting to Accounts:

Assets		Liabilities	
Bal. Dec. 31 142,000			51,000 Bal. Dec. 31

Marcy Jones, Capital		Marcy Jones, Withdrawals	
	71,800 Bal. Dec. 31	Bal. Dec. 31 38,000	

Services Revenue		Salaries Expense	
	103,000 Bal. Dec. 31	Bal. Dec. 31 27,000	

Rent Expense		Insurance Expense	
Bal. Dec. 31 9,100		Bal. Dec. 31 1,500	

Depreciation Expense		Income Summary	
Bal. Dec. 31 8,200			

Exercise 4-9

Post-Closing Trial Balance

	Debit	Credit

Name: _____

Exercise 4-10

1. _____

   _____
   _____

2.

GENERAL JOURNAL

Page____

Date		Account Titles and Explanation	PR	Debit	Credit

3.

_____
_____
_____
_____

Jozef Jones, Capital

Exercise 4-11

a.

Account Title	Adjusted Trial Balance	
	Debit	Credit
_____ Accounts payable		$ 31,000
_____ Accounts receivable	$ 48,000	
_____ Accumulated depreciation, equipment		9,000
_____ Accumulated depreciation, truck		21,000
_____ Cash	14,400	
_____ Depreciation expense	3,800	
_____ Equipment	19,000	
_____ Franchise	21,000	
_____ Gas and oil expense	7,500	
_____ Intangible asset	7,000	
_____ Interest expense	450	
_____ Interest payable		750
_____ Land not currently used in business operations	148,000	
_____ Long-term notes payable		35,000
_____ Notes payable, due February 1, 2024		7,000
_____ Notes receivable	6,000	
_____ Prepaid rent	14,000	
_____ Rent expense	51,000	
_____ Repair revenue		266,000
_____ Repair supplies	13,100	
_____ Repair supplies expense	29,000	
_____ Truck	26,000	
_____ Unearned repair revenue		12,600
_____ Vic Sopik, capital		74,900
_____ Vic Sopik, withdrawals	49,000	
Totals	$457,250	$457,250

Name: _____

Exercise 4-11 (concl'd.)

b.   **Vic Sopik, Capital**

Analysis component: _____

_____

_____

_____

Exercise 4-12   Calculations:

a.   Current assets =

b.   Property, plant and equipment =

c.   Intangible assets =

d.   Non-current investments =

e.   Total assets =

f.   Current liabilities =

g.   Non-current liabilities =

h.   Total liabilities =

i.   Total liabilities and equity =

Exercise 4-13

Sunshine Sushi			
Balance Sheet			
December 31, 2023			
Assets			
Current assets:			
Total current assets			
Non-current investments:			
Property, plant and equipment:			
Total assets			
Liabilities			
Current liabilities:			
Total current liabilities			
Non-current liabilities:			
Total liabilities			
Equity			
Total liabilities and equity			

Name: _____

Exercise 4-14

Balance Sheet			

*Fundamental Accounting Principles,*17ce, Working Papers

Exercise 4-15

Balance Sheet			

Chapter 4

Exercise 4-16

1. _____
   _____
   _____
   _____
   _____

2. Journalizing:

GENERAL JOURNAL Page____

Date	Account Titles and Explanation	PR	Debit	Credit

3. _____

Unadjusted Trial Balance

	Debit	Credit

Exercise 4-16 (cont'd.)

2, 4, 7. Posting journal entries in (b), adjustments in (d), and closing entries in (g):

Cash
Bal. Dec. 31/22 **2,000**	

Leda Svenson, Capital
	17,100 Bal. Dec. 31/22

Accounts Receivable
Bal. Dec. 31/22 **5,000**	

Leda Svenson, Withdrawals
Bal. Dec. 31/22 **-0-**	

Tutoring Revenue
	-0- Bal. Dec. 31/22

Prepaid Rent
Bal. Dec. 31/22 **3,000**	

Rent Expense
Bal. Dec. 31/22 **-0-**	

Office Equipment
Bal. Dec. 31/22 **20,000**	

Depreciation Expense
Bal. Dec. 31/22 **-0-**	

Accum. Deprec., Office Equip.
	10,000 Bal. Dec. 31/22

Advertising Expense
Bal. Dec. 31/22 **-0-**	

Unearned Revenue
	2,900 Bal. Dec. 31/22

Income Summary

Exercise 4-16 (cont'd.)

4. Journalize adjustments:

GENERAL JOURNAL

Page____

Date	Account Titles and Explanation	PR	Debit	Credit

5.

Adjusted Trial Balance

	Debit	Credit

Exercise 4-16 (cont'd.)

6. Financial statement preparation:

Income Statement

Statement of Changes in Equity

Balance Sheet

Exercise 4-16 (concl'd.)

7. Journalize closing entries:

GENERAL JOURNAL   Page____

Date	Account Titles and Explanation	PR	Debit	Credit

8. _____

Post-Closing Trial Balance

	Debit	Credit

Exercise 4-17

1. Prepare journal entries:

GENERAL JOURNAL   Page____

Date	Account Titles and Explanation	PR	Debit	Credit

Exercise 4-17 (cont'd.)

2, 3 and 5. Post journal entries, adjusting entries and closing entries to the general ledger :

Ledger as of May 31 (using the T-account format):

Cash		Supplies		Prepaid Insurance	

Printer		Laptop		Accum. Dep., Laptop	

		Accum. Dep., Printer		Accounts Payable	

Unearned Tour Revenue		Wages Payable		Emily Lee, Capital	

Emily Lee, Withdrawals	

Exercise 4-17 (cont'd.)

Parts 2, 3, 5

Deprec. Expense, Printer

Supplies Expense

Deprec. Expense, Laptop

Insurance Expense

Tour Revenue

Wages Expense

Income Summary

Exercise 4-17 (cont'd.)

3. Prepare adjusting entries:

GENERAL JOURNAL   Page____

Date	Account Titles and Explanation	PR	Debit	Credit

4. Financial statement preparation:

Income Statement

Exercise 4-17 (cont'd.)

Statement of Changes in Equity

Balance Sheet

Exercise 4-17 (concl'd.)

5. Journalize closing entries:

GENERAL JOURNAL   Page____

Date	Account Titles and Explanation	PR	Debit	Credit

6.

Post-Closing Trial Balance

	Debit	Credit

Exercise 4-18

_____
_____
_____
_____
_____
_____
_____
_____
_____
_____
_____
_____
_____
_____
_____
_____
_____
_____

Exercise 4-19

	2024	2023
Current Ratio		
Quick Ratio		

Comments: _____
_____
_____
_____
_____
_____
_____
_____
_____
_____
_____
_____
_____

Exercise 4-20

	2024	2023
Debt to equity ratio		

Comments: _____

_____

_____

_____

_____

_____

_____

_____

_____

_____

_____

_____

_____

_____

*Exercise 4-21

1. _____	Roberta Jefferson, withdrawals		9. _____	Cash
2. _____	Interest income		10. _____	Office supplies
3. _____	Accum. Deprec., machinery		11. _____	Roberta Jefferson, capital
4. _____	Service revenue		12. _____	Wages payable
5. _____	Accounts receivable		13. _____	Machinery
6. _____	Rent expense		14. _____	Insurance expense
7. _____	Deprec. Exp., machinery		15. _____	Interest expense
8. _____	Accounts payable		16. _____	Interest receivable

*Exercise 4-22

ACCOUNT	ADJUSTED TRIAL BALANCE Debit	ADJUSTED TRIAL BALANCE Credit	INCOME STATEMENT Debit	INCOME STATEMENT Credit	BALANCE SHEET AND STATEMENT OF CHANGES IN EQUITY Debit	BALANCE SHEET AND STATEMENT OF CHANGES IN EQUITY Credit
Cash	21,000					
Accounts receivable	8,200					
Trucks	48,000					
Accum. deprec., trucks		31,250				
Franchise	6,500					
Accounts payable		13,000				
Salaries payable		14,600				
Unearned revenue		2,450				
Bo Webber, capital		37,750				
Bo Webber, withdrawals	7,200					
Plumbing revenue		31,600				
Deprec. expense, trucks	12,100					
Salaries expense	17,800					
Rent expense	6,000					
Miscellaneous expense	3,850					
Totals	130,650	130,650				

*Exercise 4-23

Parts 1, 2, and 3

Musical Sensations

Work Sheet

For Year Ended December 31, 2023

Account Title	Unadjusted Trial Balance		Adjustments		Adjusted Trial Balance		Income Statement		Balance Sheet and Statement of Changes in Equity	
	Debit	Credit	Debit	Credit	Debit	Credit	Debit	Credit	Debit	Credit
Cash	7,500									
Accounts receivable	14,200									
Office supplies	790									
Musical equipment	125,000									
Accum. dep., musical equip.		21,600								
Accounts payable		4,200								
Unearned performance rev.		12,400								
Jim Daley, capital		154,300								
Jim Daley, withdrawals	52,000									
Performance revenue		138,000								
Salaries expense	86,000									
Travelling expense	45,010									
Totals	330,500	330,500								

*Exercise 4-23 (concl'd.)

Part 4

_____   **Jim Daley, Capital**

_____

_____

_____

*Exercise 4-24

1(a) _____

_____

2(a)   **GENERAL JOURNAL**   Page____

Date	Account Titles and Explanation	PR	Debit	Credit

3(a)   **Owner's Capital**

_____

_____

_____

_____

1(b) _____

_____

2(b)   **GENERAL JOURNAL**   Page____

Date	Account Titles and Explanation	PR	Debit	Credit

3(b)   **Owner's Capital**

_____

_____

_____

*Exercise 4-25

	Debit	Credit
Rent revenue		97,000
Salaries expense	35,000	
Insurance expense	4,100	
Dock rental expense	11,700	
Boat supplies expense	5,920	
Depreciation expense, boats	21,200	
Totals		
Profit		
Totals		

Closing Entries

GENERAL JOURNAL   Page____

Date	Account Titles and Explanation	PR	Debit	Credit

Name: _____

Problem 4-1A

Income Statement

Statement of Owner's Equity

Name: _____

Problem 4-1A (cont'd.)

Balance Sheet

Problem 4-1A (concl'd.)

GENERAL JOURNAL

Page____

Date	Account Titles and Explanation	PR	Debit	Credit

Name: _____

Problem 4-2A

Part 1   **GENERAL JOURNAL**   Page____

Date	Account Titles and Explanation	PR	Debit	Credit

Name: _____

Problem 4-2A (concl'd.)

Part 2

Post-Closing Trial Balance

Problem 4-3A

Income Statement

Statement of Changes in Equity

Problem 4-3A (concl'd.)

Balance Sheet			

Analysis component:

_____

_____

_____

_____

_____

_____

GENERAL JOURNAL

Page____

Date	Account Titles and Explanation	PR	Debit	Credit

Income Statement

Statement of Changes in Equity

*Fundamental Accounting Principles,*17ce, Working Papers

Problem 4-5A (concl'd.)

	Balance Sheet			

Analysis component:

_____

_____

_____

_____

_____

Name: _____

Problem 4-6A

Part 1

GENERAL JOURNAL

Page____

Date	Account Titles and Explanation	PR	Debit	Credit

Problem 4-6A (cont'd.)

Part 2

Adjusted Trial Balance		
	Debit	Credit

Name: _____

Problem 4-6A (concl'd.)

Part 3

GENERAL JOURNAL

Page____

Date	Account Titles and Explanation	PR	Debit	Credit

Problem 4-7A

Income Statement

Statement of Changes in Equity

Problem 4-7A (concl'd.)

	Balance Sheet			

Analysis component:

Problem 4-8A

Part 1

Income Statement		

Part 2

Nolan Apex, Capital

Income Statement		

Statement of Changes in Equity		

Problem 4-9A (concl'd.)

Balance Sheet

Analysis component:

_____
_____
_____
_____
_____
_____
_____
_____

Problem 4-10A

Part 1

_____   ## Wyett North, Capital
_____
_____
_____

Part 2

	Balance Sheet			

Name: _____

Problem 4-10A (concl'd.)

Part 3

Current Ratio	
Debt to equity ratio	

Analysis component:

_____
_____
_____
_____
_____
_____
_____
_____

Name: _____

Problem 4-11A

Part 1. Use either the balance column format or T-accounts; both are provided.

GENERAL LEDGER

Cash — ACCOUNT NO. 10

DATE	EXPLANATION	PR	DEBIT	CREDIT	BALANCE

Accounts Receivable — ACCOUNT NO. 10

DATE	EXPLANATION	PR	DEBIT	CREDIT	BALANCE

Office Supplies — ACCOUNT NO. 12

DATE	EXPLANATION	PR	DEBIT	CREDIT	BALANCE

Prepaid Insurance — ACCOUNT NO. 12

DATE	EXPLANATION	PR	DEBIT	CREDIT	BALANCE

Furniture — ACCOUNT NO. 16

DATE	EXPLANATION	PR	DEBIT	CREDIT	BALANCE

Accumulated Depreciation, Furniture — ACCOUNT NO. 16

DATE	EXPLANATION	PR	DEBIT	CREDIT	BALANCE

Problem 4-11A (cont'd.)

Computer Equipment ACCOUNT NO. 167

DATE	EXPLANATION	PR	DEBIT	CREDIT	BALANCE

Accumulated Depreciation, Computer Equipment ACCOUNT NO. 168

DATE	EXPLANATION	PR	DEBIT	CREDIT	BALANCE

Accounts Payable ACCOUNT NO. 201

DATE	EXPLANATION	PR	DEBIT	CREDIT	BALANCE

Salaries Payable ACCOUNT NO. 209

DATE	EXPLANATION	PR	DEBIT	CREDIT	BALANCE

Sam Near, Capital ACCOUNT NO. 301

DATE	EXPLANATION	PR	DEBIT	CREDIT	BALANCE

Sam Near, Withdrawals ACCOUNT NO. 302

DATE	EXPLANATION	PR	DEBIT	CREDIT	BALANCE

Commissions Revenue ACCOUNT NO. 405

DATE	EXPLANATION	PR	DEBIT	CREDIT	BALANCE

Depreciation Expense, Furniture ACCOUNT NO. 610

DATE	EXPLANATION	PR	DEBIT	CREDIT	BALANCE

Problem 4-11A (cont'd.)

Depreciation Expense, Computer Equipment   . ACCOUNT NO. 61█

DATE	EXPLANATION	PR	DEBIT	CREDIT	BALANCE

Salaries Expense   ACCOUNT NO. 62█

DATE	EXPLANATION	PR	DEBIT	CREDIT	BALANCE

Insurance Expense   ACCOUNT NO. 63█

DATE	EXPLANATION	PR	DEBIT	CREDIT	BALANCE

Rent Expense   ACCOUNT NO. 64█

DATE	EXPLANATION	PR	DEBIT	CREDIT	BALANCE

Office Supplies Expense   ACCOUNT NO. 65█

DATE	EXPLANATION	PR	DEBIT	CREDIT	BALANCE

Repairs Expense   ACCOUNT NO. 684

DATE	EXPLANATION	PR	DEBIT	CREDIT	BALANCE

Telephone Expense   ACCOUNT NO. 688

DATE	EXPLANATION	PR	DEBIT	CREDIT	BALANCE

Problem 4-11A (cont'd.)

	Income Summary			ACCOUNT NO. 901	
DATE	EXPLANATION	PR	DEBIT	CREDIT	BALANCE

Part 1.　Use either T-accounts or the balance column format; both are provided.

Cash　　101

Accum. Deprec, Furniture　　161

Computer Equipment　　167

Accum. Deprec, Computer Equip　　168

Accounts Payable　　201

Accounts Receivable　　106

Salaries Payable　　209

Office Supplies　　124

Sam Near, Capital　　301

Prepaid Insurance　　128

Sam Near, Withdrawals　　302

Commissions Revenue　　405

Furniture　　160

Problem 4-11A (cont'd.)

Part 1. Use either T-accounts or the balance column format; both are provided.

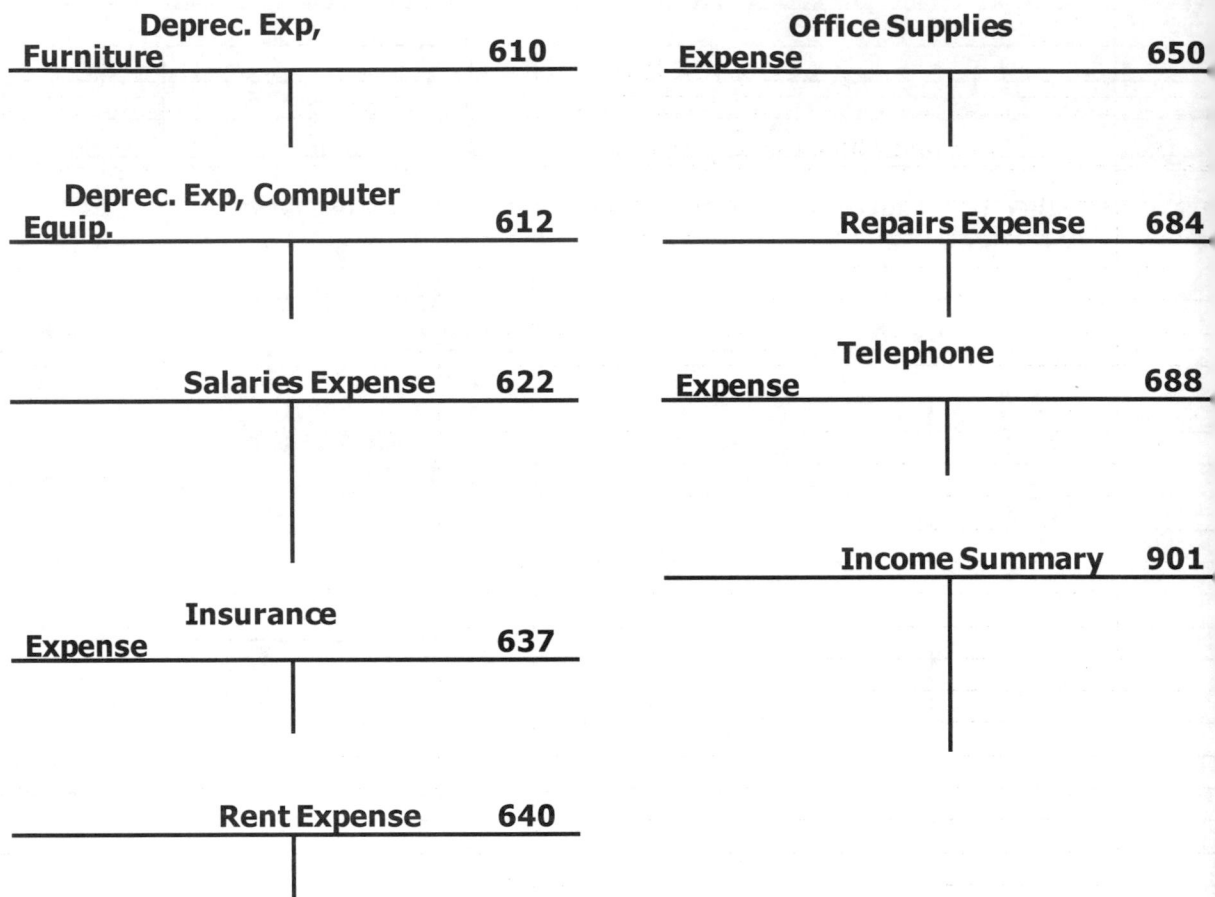

| Deprec. Exp, Furniture | 610 | | Office Supplies Expense | 650 |

| Deprec. Exp, Computer Equip. | 612 | | Repairs Expense | 684 |

| Salaries Expense | 622 | | Telephone Expense | 688 |

| Insurance Expense | 637 | | Income Summary | 901 |

| Rent Expense | 640 |

Problem 4-11A (cont'd.)

Part 2. Transactions for June:

GENERAL JOURNAL   Page____

Date	Account Titles and Explanation	PR	Debit	Credit

Name: _____

Problem 4-11A (cont'd.)

Part 2. Transactions for June (cont'd.)

GENERAL JOURNAL

Page___

Date		Account Titles and Explanation	PR	Debit	Credit

Problem 4-11A (cont'd.)

Part 3. Adjusting entries:

GENERAL JOURNAL

Page____

Date	Account Titles and Explanation	PR	Debit	Credit

Part 4. Financial statements:

Income Statement

Name: _____

Problem 4-11A (cont'd.)

Statement of Changes in Equity

Balance Sheet

Problem 4-11A (concl'd.)

Part 5. Closing entries:

GENERAL JOURNAL

Page____

Date	Account Titles and Explanation	PR	Debit	Credit

Part 6

Post-Closing Trial Balance

	Debit	Credit

Name: _____

Problem 4-12A

a.

	2020	2019
Current ratio		
Quick ratio		
Debt to equity ratio		

b. Comments:

_____
_____
_____
_____
_____
_____
_____
_____
_____
_____
_____
_____

Problem 4-13A

Part 1

GENERAL JOURNAL

Page____

Date		Account Titles and Explanation	PR	Debit	Credit
a.					
b.					
c.					
d.					
e.					
f.					

*Problem 4-13A (concl'd.)

Part 2

GENERAL JOURNAL

Page___

Date		Account Titles and Explanation	PR	Debit	Credit

Part 3

GENERAL JOURNAL

Page___

Date		Account Titles and Explanation	PR	Debit	Credit

Silva Rentals

Work Sheet

For Year Ended March 31, 2023

Account Title	Unadjusted Trial Balance Debit	Unadjusted Trial Balance Credit	Adjustments Debit	Adjustments Credit	Adjusted Trial Balance Debit	Adjusted Trial Balance Credit	Income Statement Debit	Income Statement Credit	Balance Sheet and Statement of Changes in Equity Debit	Balance Sheet and Statement of Changes in Equity Credit
Cash	7,000									
Rent receivable	31,000									
Office supplies	2,250									
Notes receivable, due 2023	46,000									
Furniture	16,000									
Building	216,000									
Land	41,000									
Patent	9,600									
Accounts payable		13,750								
Long-term note payable		175,000								
Stephen Silva, capital		90,250								
Stephen Silva, withdrawals	92,000									
Rent revenue		328,800								
Office salaries expense	52,000									
Interest expense	5,250									
Advertising expense	14,600									
Janitorial expense	41,000									
Utilities expense	34,100									
Totals	607,800	607,800								

Parts 1, 2, and 3

Trenton Consulting

Work Sheet

For Year Ended June 30, 2023

Account Title	Unadjusted Trial Balance		Adjustments		Adjusted Trial Balance		Income Statement		Balance Sheet and Statement of Changes in Equity	
	Debit	Credit	Debit	Credit	Debit	Credit	Debit	Credit	Debit	Credit
Cash	680									
Accounts receivable	2,900									
Prepaid rent	3,660									
Equipment	9,600									
Accounts payable		1,730								
Toni Trenton, capital		26,650								
Toni Trenton, withdrawals	6,880									
Consulting revenue		30,200								
Wages expense	24,920									
Insurance expense	1,620									
Rent expense	8,320									
Totals	58,580	58,580								

Name: _____

Problem 4-15A (concl'd.)

Part 4

_____   **Toni Trenton, Capital**
_____   _____
_____
_____

Analysis component:

_____
_____
_____
_____
_____
_____
_____

*Problem 4-16A

Parts 1 and 2

Challenger Construction

Work Sheet

For Year Ended September 30, 2023

Account Title	Unadjusted Trial Balance Debit	Unadjusted Trial Balance Credit	Adjustments Debit	Adjustments Credit	Adjusted Trial Balance Debit	Adjusted Trial Balance Credit	Income Statement Debit	Income Statement Credit	Balance Sheet and Statement of Changes in Equity Debit	Balance Sheet and Statement of Changes in Equity Credit
Cash	22,000									
Supplies	17,200									
Prepaid insurance	9,600									
Land not currently used	50,000									
Equipment	106,000									
Accum. deprec., equipment		40,500								
Copyright	6,000									
Accounts payable		8,100								
Interest payable										
Wages payable										
Long-term notes payable		50,000								
Chris Challenger, capital		71,000								
Chris Challenger, withdrawals	68,000									
Construction revenue		255,620								
Deprec. Expense, equipment										
Wages expense	96,000									
Interest expense	1,200									
Insurance expense										
Rent expense	26,400									
Supplies expense										
Business taxes expense	10,000									
Repairs expense	5,020	⌘								
Utilities expense	7,800									
Totals	425,220	425,220								

Problem 4-16A (cont'd.)

art 1

djusting entries:

GENERAL JOURNAL

Page____

Date	Account Titles and Explanation	PR	Debit	Credit
a.				
b.				
c.				
d.				
e.				
f.				

*Problem 4-16A (cont'd.)

Part 2

Closing entries:

GENERAL JOURNAL   Page___

Date	Account Titles and Explanation	PR	Debit	Credit

Problem 4-16A (cont'd.)

Part 3

Income Statement

Statement of Changes in Equity

*Problem 4-16A (concl'd.)

Balance Sheet			

Analysis component:

a. _____

_____

b. _____

_____

_____

Income Statement

Statement of Owner's Equity

Name: _____

Problem 4-1B (concl'd.)

Balance Sheet			

GENERAL JOURNAL

Page____

Date		Account Titles and Explanation	PR	Debit	Credit

Problem 4-2B

Part 1

GENERAL JOURNAL

Date	Account Titles and Explanation	PR	Debit	Credit

Part 2

Post-Closing Trial Balance

	Debit	Credit

roblem 4-3B

Income Statement

Statement of Changes in Equity

Name: _____

Problem 4-3B (concl'd.)

	Balance Sheet			

Analysis component:

_____

_____

_____

_____

_____

_____

GENERAL JOURNAL

Page____

Date		Account Titles and Explanation	PR	Debit	Credit

Name: _____

Problem 4-5B

Income Statement

Statement of Changes in Equity

Problem 4-5B (concl'd.)

Balance Sheet

Analysis component:

Name: _____

Problem 4-6B

Part 1

GENERAL JOURNAL

Page__

Date		Account Titles and Explanation	PR	Debit	Credit

Adjusted Trial Balance

	Debit	Credit

Problem 4-6B (concl'd.)

Part 3

GENERAL JOURNAL   Page__

Date	Account Titles and Explanation	PR	Debit	Credit

Income Statement

Statement of Changes in Equity

Name: _____

Problem 4-7B (concl'd.)

Balance Sheet			

Analysis component:

_____

_____

_____

_____

_____

_____

Problem 4-8B

Part 1

	Income Statement		

Part 2

_____

_____

_____

_____

Grant Greenway, Capital

Problem 4-9B

Income Statement

Statement of Changes in Equity

Chapter 4

Name: _____

Problem 4-9B (concl'd.)

Balance Sheet

Analysis component:

Problem 4-10B

Part 1

_____

Jan Delta, Capital

Part 2

Balance Sheet			

Name: _____

Problem 4-10B (concl'd.)

Part 3

Current Ratio	
Debt to equity ratio	

_____
_____
_____
_____
_____
_____
_____
_____

Problem 4-11B

Part 1. Use either the balance column format or T-accounts; both are provided.

GENERAL LEDGER

Cash   ACCOUNT NO. 10

DATE	EXPLANATION	PR	DEBIT	CREDIT	BALANCE

Accounts Receivable   ACCOUNT NO. 10

DATE	EXPLANATION	PR	DEBIT	CREDIT	BALANCE

Office Supplies   ACCOUNT NO. 124

DATE	EXPLANATION	PR	DEBIT	CREDIT	BALANCE

Prepaid Insurance   ACCOUNT NO. 128

DATE	EXPLANATION	PR	DEBIT	CREDIT	BALANCE

Land   ACCOUNT NO. 170

DATE	EXPLANATION	PR	DEBIT	CREDIT	BALANCE

Buildings   ACCOUNT NO. 173

DATE	EXPLANATION	PR	DEBIT	CREDIT	BALANCE

Accumulated Depreciation, Buildings   ACCOUNT NO. 174

DATE	EXPLANATION	PR	DEBIT	CREDIT	BALANCE

Problem 4-11B (cont'd.)

Accounts Payable   ACCOUNT NO. 201

DATE	EXPLANATION	PR	DEBIT	CREDIT	BALANCE

Salaries Payable   ACCOUNT NO. 209

DATE	EXPLANATION	PR	DEBIT	CREDIT	BALANCE

Amy Young, Capital   ACCOUNT NO. 301

DATE	EXPLANATION	PR	DEBIT	CREDIT	BALANCE

Amy Young, Withdrawals   ACCOUNT NO. 302

DATE	EXPLANATION	PR	DEBIT	CREDIT	BALANCE

Storage Revenue   ACCOUNT NO. 401

DATE	EXPLANATION	PR	DEBIT	CREDIT	BALANCE

Depreciation Expense, Buildings   ACCOUNT NO. 606

DATE	EXPLANATION	PR	DEBIT	CREDIT	BALANCE

Salaries Expense   ACCOUNT NO. 622

DATE	EXPLANATION	PR	DEBIT	CREDIT	BALANCE

Problem 4-11B (cont'd.)

Insurance Expense — ACCOUNT NO. 63

DATE	EXPLANATION	PR	DEBIT	CREDIT	BALANCE

Equipment Rental Expense — ACCOUNT NO. 64

DATE	EXPLANATION	PR	DEBIT	CREDIT	BALANCE

Office Supplies Expense — ACCOUNT NO. 650

DATE	EXPLANATION	PR	DEBIT	CREDIT	BALANCE

Repairs Expense — ACCOUNT NO. 684

DATE	EXPLANATION	PR	DEBIT	CREDIT	BALANCE

Telephone Expense — ACCOUNT NO. 688

DATE	EXPLANATION	PR	DEBIT	CREDIT	BALANCE

Income Summary — ACCOUNT NO. 901

DATE	EXPLANATION	PR	DEBIT	CREDIT	BALANCE

*Fundamental Accounting Principles,*17ce, Working Paper

Name: _____

Problem 4-11B (cont'd.)

Cash	101

Accounts Payable	201

Salaries Payable	209

Accounts Receivable	106

Amy Young, Capital	301

Amy Young, Withdrawals	302

Office Supplies	124

Storage Revenue	405

Prepaid Insurance	128

Deprec. Exp., Buildings	606

Land	170

Salaries Expense	622

Buildings	173

Insurance Expense	637

Accum. Deprec., Buildings	174

Equipment Rental Expense	640

Problem 4-11B (cont'd.)

Office Supplies Expense	650		Telephone Expense	688

	Repairs Expense	684		Income Summary	901

Part 2. Transactions for July:

GENERAL JOURNAL

Page___

Date	Account Titles and Explanation	PR	Debit	Credit

Problem 4-11B (cont'd.)

Part 2. Transactions for July (cont'd.)

GENERAL JOURNAL

Page____

Date		Account Titles and Explanation	PR	Debit	Credit

Problem 4-11B (cont'd.)

Part 3. Adjusting entries:

GENERAL JOURNAL   Page____

Date	Account Titles and Explanation	PR	Debit	Credit

Part 4

Income Statement

Statement of Changes in Equity

Balance Sheet

Name: _____

Problem 4-11B (concl'd.)

Part 5. Closing entries:

GENERAL JOURNAL Page____

Date		Account Titles and Explanation	PR	Debit	Credit

Part 6

Post-Closing Trial Balance

	Debit	Credit

Problem 4-12B

	2020	2019
Current ratio		
Quick ratio		
Debt to equity ratio		

. Comments:

_____
_____
_____
_____
_____
_____
_____
_____
_____
_____
_____
_____
_____
_____
_____

*Problem 4-13B (cont'd.)

Part 1

GENERAL JOURNAL

Page___

Date	Account Titles and Explanation	PR	Debit	Credit

Problem 4-13B (concl'd.)

art 2

GENERAL JOURNAL

Page____

Date		Account Titles and Explanation	PR	Debit	Credit

art 3

GENERAL JOURNAL

Page____

Date		Account Titles and Explanation	PR	Debit	Credit

*Problem 4-14B

Parts 1, 2, and 3

Daimler Tours

Work Sheet

For Year Ended July 31, 2023

Account Title	Unadjusted Trial Balance		Adjustments		Adjusted Trial Balance		Income Statement		Balance Sheet and Statement of Changes in Equity	
	Debit	Credit	Debit	Credit	Debit	Credit	Debit	Credit	Debit	Credit
Cash	9,100									
Accounts receivable	18,700									
Notes receivable	16,000									
Prepaid insurance	5,100									
Furniture	6,750									
Accounts payable		6,925								
Unearned tour revenue		12,430								
Jan Rider, capital		60,975								
Jan Rider, withdrawals	-0-									
Tour revenue		16,700								
Wages expense	41,380									
Totals	97,030	97,030								

*Fundamental Accounting Principles,*17ce, Working Paper

Problem 4-15B

Parts 1, 2, and 3

Tucker Photographers

Work Sheet

For Year Ended December 31, 2023

Account Title	Unadjusted Trial Balance		Adjustments		Adjusted Trial Balance		Income Statement		Balance Sheet and Statement of Changes in Equity	
	Debit	Credit	Debit	Credit	Debit	Credit	Debit	Credit	Debit	Credit
Cash	9,100									
Accounts receivable	13,000									
Prepaid equipment rental	3,860									
Automobile	49,000									
Accum. deprec., automobile		-0-								
Accounts payable		1,920								
Unearned revenue		5,740								
Jim Tucker, capital		65,700								
Jim Tucker, withdrawals	2,600									
Service Revenue		8,400								
Deprec. Expense, automobile	-0-									
Equipment rental expense	4,200									
Totals	81,760	81,760								

Name: _____

*Problem 4-15B (concl'd.)

Part 4

Jim Tucker, Capital

Analysis component:

Problem 4-16B

Parts 1 and 2

Webster Demolition Company
Work Sheet
For Year Ended June 30, 2023

Account Title	Unadjusted Trial Balance Debit	Unadjusted Trial Balance Credit	Adjustments Debit	Adjustments Credit	Adjusted Trial Balance Debit	Adjusted Trial Balance Credit	Income Statement Debit	Income Statement Credit	Balance Sheet and Statement of Changes in Equity Debit	Balance Sheet and Statement of Changes in Equity Credit
Cash	4,500									
Supplies	8,200									
Prepaid insurance	7,300									
Equipment	72,000									
Accum. deprec., equipment		5,000								
Accounts payable		9,100								
Interest payable										
Wages payable										
Long-term notes payable		45,000								
Rusty Webster, capital		21,400								
Rusty Webster, withdrawals	2,100									
Demolition revenue		83,300								
Deprec. expense, equipment										
Wages expense	27,400									
Interest expense	1,100									
Insurance expense										
Rent expense	24,400									
Supplies expense										
Business tax expense	4,200									
Repairs expense	4,200									
Utilities expense	8,400									
Totals	163,800	163,800								

Name: _____

*Problem 4-16B (cont'd.)

Part 1

Adjusting entries:

GENERAL JOURNAL

Page___

Date	Account Titles and Explanation	PR	Debit	Credit
a.				
b.				
c.				
d.				
e.				
f.				

Name: _____

Problem 4-16B (cont'd.)

Part 2

Closing entries:

GENERAL JOURNAL

Page____

Date	Account Titles and Explanation	PR	Debit	Credit

Name: _____

*Problem 4-16B (cont'd.)

Part 3

Income Statement

Statement of Changes in Equity

Problem 4-16B (concl'd.)

Balance Sheet			

Analysis component:

a. _____
_____
_____
_____

b. _____
_____
_____
_____

Fundamental Accounting Principles, 17ce, Working Papers

427

Cumulative Problem

Part 1   **Echo Systems**

GENERAL JOURNAL

Page___

Date	Account Titles and Explanation	PR	Debit	Credit

Cumulative Problem (cont'd.)

GENERAL JOURNAL

Page____

Date	Account Titles and Explanation	PR	Debit	Credit

Cumulative Problem (cont'd.)

GENERAL LEDGER

Cash   ACCOUNT NO. 101

DATE	EXPLANATION	PR	DEBIT	CREDIT	BALANCE
2023 Dec. 31	Balance				89,090

Accounts Receivable   ACCOUNT NO. 106

DATE	EXPLANATION	PR	DEBIT	CREDIT	BALANCE
2023 Dec. 31	Balance				5,700

Computer Supplies   ACCOUNT NO. 126

DATE	EXPLANATION	PR	DEBIT	CREDIT	BALANCE
2023 Dec. 31	Balance				1,440

Prepaid Insurance   ACCOUNT NO. 128

DATE	EXPLANATION	PR	DEBIT	CREDIT	BALANCE
2023 Dec. 31	Balance				3,240

Prepaid Rent   ACCOUNT NO. 131

DATE	EXPLANATION	PR	DEBIT	CREDIT	BALANCE
2023 Dec. 31	Balance				2,250

Office Equipment   ACCOUNT NO. 163

DATE	EXPLANATION	PR	DEBIT	CREDIT	BALANCE
2023 Dec. 31	Balance				18,000

Accumulated Depreciation, Office Equipment   ACCOUNT NO. 164

DATE	EXPLANATION	PR	DEBIT	CREDIT	BALANCE
2023 Dec. 31	Balance				1,500

Cumulative Problem (cont'd.)

Computer Equipment   ACCOUNT NO. 167

DATE	EXPLANATION	PR	DEBIT	CREDIT	BALANCE
2023 Dec. 31	Balance				36,000

Accumulated Depreciation, Computer Equipment   ACCOUNT NO. 168

DATE	EXPLANATION	PR	DEBIT	CREDIT	BALANCE
2023 Dec. 31	Balance				2,250

Accounts Payable   ACCOUNT NO. 201

DATE	EXPLANATION	PR	DEBIT	CREDIT	BALANCE
2023 Dec. 31	Balance				2,310

Wages Payable   ACCOUNT NO. 210

DATE	EXPLANATION	PR	DEBIT	CREDIT	BALANCE
2023 Dec. 31	Balance				800

Unearned Computer Services Revenue   ACCOUNT NO. 236

DATE	EXPLANATION	PR	DEBIT	CREDIT	BALANCE
2023 Dec. 31	Balance				3,000

Mary Graham, Capital   ACCOUNT NO. 301

DATE	EXPLANATION	PR	DEBIT	CREDIT	BALANCE
2023 Dec. 31	Balance				144,000

Mary Graham, Withdrawals   ACCOUNT NO. 302

DATE	EXPLANATION	PR	DEBIT	CREDIT	BALANCE
2023 Dec. 31	Balance				14,400

Cumulative Problem (cont'd.)

Computer Services Revenue   ACCOUNT NO. 403

DATE	EXPLANATION	PR	DEBIT	CREDIT	BALANCE
2023 Dec. 31	Balance				52,200

Depreciation Expense, Office Equipment   ACCOUNT NO. 612

DATE	EXPLANATION	PR	DEBIT	CREDIT	BALANCE
2023 Dec. 31	Balance				1,500

Depreciation Expense, Computer Equipment   ACCOUNT NO. 613

DATE	EXPLANATION	PR	DEBIT	CREDIT	BALANCE
2023 Dec. 31	Balance				2,250

Wages Expense   ACCOUNT NO. 623

DATE	EXPLANATION	PR	DEBIT	CREDIT	BALANCE
2023 Dec. 31	Balance				6,200

Insurance Expense   ACCOUNT NO. 637

DATE	EXPLANATION	PR	DEBIT	CREDIT	BALANCE
2023 Dec. 31	Balance				1,080

Rent Expense   ACCOUNT NO. 640

DATE	EXPLANATION	PR	DEBIT	CREDIT	BALANCE
2023 Dec. 31	Balance				6,750

Computer Supplies Expense   ACCOUNT NO. 652

DATE	EXPLANATION	PR	DEBIT	CREDIT	BALANCE
2023 Dec. 31	Balance				5,430

Cumulative Problem (cont'd.)

Advertising Expense   ACCOUNT NO. 655

DATE	EXPLANATION	PR	DEBIT	CREDIT	BALANCE
2023 Dec. 31	Balance				5,820

Mileage Expense   ACCOUNT NO. 676

DATE	EXPLANATION	PR	DEBIT	CREDIT	BALANCE
2023 Dec. 31	Balance				2,800

Repairs Expense, Computer   ACCOUNT NO. 684

DATE	EXPLANATION	PR	DEBIT	CREDIT	BALANCE
2023 Dec. 31	Balance				2,610

Charitable Donations Expense   ACCOUNT NO. 699

DATE	EXPLANATION	PR	DEBIT	CREDIT	BALANCE
2023 Dec. 31	Balance				1,500

Income Summary   ACCOUNT NO. 901

DATE	EXPLANATION	PR	DEBIT	CREDIT	BALANCE
2023 Dec. 31	Balance				

Cumulative Problem (concl'd.)

Part 2

ECHO SYSTEMS
Post-Closing Trial Balance
December 31, 2023

	Debit	Credit

Quick Study 5-1

    a) Sales discount
    b) Credit period
    c) Discount period
    d) FOB destination
    e) FOB shipping point
    f) Gross profit
    g) Merchandise inventory
    h) Purchases discount

_____ 1. Goods a company owns and expects to sell to its customers.
_____ 2. Time period that can pass before a customer's full payment is due.
_____ 3. Seller's description of a cash discount granted to buyers in return for early payment.
_____ 4. Ownership of goods is transferred when the seller delivers goods to the carrier.
_____ 5. Purchaser's description of a cash discount received from a supplier of goods.
_____ 6. Difference between net sales and the cost of goods sold.
_____ 7. Time period in which a cash discount is available.
_____ 8. Ownership of goods is transferred when delivered to the buyer's place of business.

Quick Study 5-2

_____
_____
_____

Quick Study 5-3

1. (1)   **Computation of goods available for sale**

_____
_____
_____

   (2)   **Computation of cost of goods sold**

_____
_____
_____
_____
_____

   (3)   **Computation of gross profit**

_____
_____
_____

2.   **Computation of net income**

           <u>   **McNeil Merchandising Company**   </u>

_____
_____
_____
_____
_____

           <u>   **Krug Service Company**   </u>

_____
_____
_____
_____
_____

Quick Study 5-4

a. _____
_____

b. _____
_____

c. _____
_____

d. _____
_____
_____

Quick Study 5-5

GENERAL JOURNAL   Page____

Date	Account Titles and Explanation	PR	Debit	Credit

Quick Study 5-6

GENERAL JOURNAL   Page____

Date	Account Titles and Explanation	PR	Debit	Credit

Quick Study 5-7

GENERAL JOURNAL					Page____
Date	Account Titles and Explanation	PR	Debit	Credit	

Quick Study 5-8

GENERAL JOURNAL					Page____
Date	Account Titles and Explanation	PR	Debit	Credit	

Quick Study 5-9

	A	B	C	D	E

Quick Study 5-10

a. _____

b. _____

c. _____

d. _____

e. _____

Quick Study 5-11

a. _____

b. _____

Quick Study 5-12

a. _____

b. _____

Quick Study 5-13

a. _____

_____

b. _____

c. _____

GENERAL JOURNAL   Page____

Date	Account Titles and Explanation	PR	Debit	Credit

d. _____

GENERAL JOURNAL   Page____

Date	Account Titles and Explanation	PR	Debit	Credit

Quick Study 5-14

GENERAL JOURNAL   Page____

Date	Account Titles and Explanation	PR	Debit	Credit

Quick Study 5-15

GENERAL JOURNAL   Page____

Date	Account Titles and Explanation	PR	Debit	Credit

Quick Study 5-16

GENERAL JOURNAL   Page____

Date		Account Titles and Explanation	PR	Debit	Credit

Quick Study 5-17

a. _____

_____

b. _____

_____

c.   ### GENERAL JOURNAL   Page____

Date		Account Titles and Explanation	PR	Debit	Credit

d.   ### GENERAL JOURNAL   Page____

Date		Account Titles and Explanation	PR	Debit	Credit

Quick Study 5-18

GENERAL JOURNAL

Page____

Date	Account Titles and Explanation	PR	Debit	Credit

Quick Study 5-19

GENERAL JOURNAL

Page____

Date	Account Titles and Explanation	PR	Debit	Credit

Quick Study 5-20

GENERAL JOURNAL   Page____

Date	Account Titles and Explanation	PR	Debit	Credit

Quick Study 5-21

GENERAL JOURNAL   Page____

Date	Account Titles and Explanation	PR	Debit	Credit

Gross profit from sales = _____

_____

_____

_____

_____

Name: _____

Quick Study 5-22

GENERAL JOURNAL

Page____

Date		Account Titles and Explanation	PR	Debit	Credit

Name: _____

Quick Study 5-23

a. Classified Multi-Step

Income Statement			

b. Single-Step

Income Statement			

Fundamental Accounting Principles, 17ce, Working Papers

Name: _____

Quick Study 5-24

	(a)	(b)	(c)	(d)

Calculations:

_____
_____
_____
_____
_____

Quick Study 5-25

	Carrier	Lennox	Trane	York

Calculations:

_____
_____
_____
_____
_____

Name: _____

Quick Study 5-26

_____
_____
_____
_____
_____

Quick Study 5-27

_____
_____
_____
_____
_____

Quick Study 5-28

_____
_____
_____
_____
_____

Quick Study 5-29

_____
_____
_____
_____
_____

*Quick Study 5-30

QS5-14 - Periodic		GENERAL JOURNAL			Page____
Date		**Account Titles and Explanation**	**PR**	**Debit**	**Credit**

QS5-15 - Periodic		GENERAL JOURNAL			Page____
Date		**Account Titles and Explanation**	**PR**	**Debit**	**Credit**

*Quick Study 5-30(Continued)

QS5-16 - Periodic   GENERAL JOURNAL   Page____

Date		Account Titles and Explanation	PR	Debit	Credit

*Quick Study 5-31

QS5-18 - Periodic   GENERAL JOURNAL   Page____

Date		Account Titles and Explanation	PR	Debit	Credit

*Quick Study 5-31(Continued)

QS5-19 - Periodic   GENERAL JOURNAL   Page____

Date		Account Titles and Explanation	PR	Debit	Credit

QS5-20 - Periodic   GENERAL JOURNAL   Page____

Date		Account Titles and Explanation	PR	Debit	Credit

Name: _____

*Quick Study 5-32

_____
_____
_____
_____
_____
_____
_____
_____
_____
_____
_____
_____
_____
_____

*Quick Study 5-33

	(a)	(b)	(c)	(d)

Calculations:

_____
_____
_____
_____
_____
_____

*Quick Study 5-34

GENERAL JOURNAL   Page____

Date		Account Titles and Explanation	PR	Debit	Credit

*Quick Study 5-35

GENERAL JOURNAL   Page____

Date		Account Titles and Explanation	PR	Debit	Credit

*Quick Study 5-36

GENERAL JOURNAL   Page____

Date		Account Titles and Explanation	PR	Debit	Credit

Name: _____

*Quick Study 5-37

GENERAL JOURNAL   Page____

Date	Account Titles and Explanation	PR	Debit	Credit

Name: _____

Exercise 5-1

	a	b	c	d	e
Net sales..........................	$ 208,800	$ 165,000	$ 73,800		
Cost of goods sold..............			41,600	303,000	205,600
Gross profit from sales.......	108,200				75,200
Operating expenses............	91,600	93,000		106,000	
Profit (loss).......................		(31,000)	(5,900)	57,000	(28,400)

Chapter 5

Name: _____

Exercise 5-2

GENERAL JOURNAL   Page____

Date	Account Titles and Explanation	PR	Debit	Credit

Exercise 5-3

GENERAL JOURNAL

Date	Account Titles and Explanation	PR	Debit	Credit

Exercise 5-4

GENERAL JOURNAL

Page____

Date	Account Titles and Explanation	PR	Debit	Credit

Fundamental Accounting Principles, 17ce, Working Papers

Exercise 5-5

GENERAL JOURNAL

Date	Account Titles and Explanation	PR	Debit	Credit

Name: _____

Exercise 5-5 (concl'd.)

GENERAL JOURNAL   Page____

Date	Account Titles and Explanation	PR	Debit	Credit

Name: _____

Exercise 5-6

GENERAL JOURNAL

Page____

Date		Account Titles and Explanation	PR	Debit	Credit

Exercise 5-6 (concl'd.)

GENERAL JOURNAL

Page____

Date	Account Titles and Explanation	PR	Debit	Credit

Exercise 5-7

a. **Entries journalized by Wilson Purchasing:**

GENERAL JOURNAL   Page____

Date	Account Titles and Explanation	PR	Debit	Credit

b. **Entries journalized by Happy Sales:**

GENERAL JOURNAL   Page____

Date	Account Titles and Explanation	PR	Debit	Credit

Exercise 5-7 (concl'd.)

GENERAL JOURNAL   Page____

Date	Account Titles and Explanation	PR	Debit	Credit

Analysis component:

_____
_____
_____
_____
_____
_____
_____
_____
_____
_____
_____
_____
_____
_____

Exercise 5-8

1.		6.	
2.		7.	
3.		8.	
4.		9.	
5.		10.	

Name: _____

Exercise 5-9

Merchandise Inventory	Cost of Goods Sold

Analysis component:

_____
_____
_____
_____
_____
_____
_____
_____
_____
_____
_____
_____

Exercise 5-10

(a) _____
(b) _____
(c) _____
(d) _____

Analysis component:

_____
_____
_____
_____
_____
_____
_____
_____

Name: _____

Exercise 5-11

	Company A		Company B	
	2023	2022	2023	2022
Sales	$263,000	$187,000		$48,500
Sales discounts	2,630		1,200	570
Sales returns and allowances		16,700	6,200	
Net sales		$168,950		$45,500
Cost of goods sold	157,100		57,700	
Gross profit from sales	$ 51,700		$ 49,100	$ 22,100
Selling expenses	18,620	19,700	25,700	
Administrative expenses	26,300		30,400	9,700
Total operating expenses		$ 47,400		
Profit (loss)		$ 15,100		$ 2,700
Gross profit ratio				

Calculations:

_____
_____
_____
_____
_____
_____
_____

Analysis component:

_____
_____
_____
_____
_____
_____
_____

Exercise 5-12

Income Statement

Analysis component:

_____

_____

_____

_____

_____

_____

_____

_____

Exercise 5-13

Part a

GENERAL JOURNAL

Page____

Date	Account Titles and Explanation	PR	Debit	Credit

Exercise 5-13 (Continued)

Note: A work sheet is not required for this question. The following shows the adjusted balances.

	Unadjusted Trial Balance		Adjustments		Adjusted Trial Balance	
Account	*Debit*	*Credit*	*Debit*	*Credit*	*Debit*	*Credit*
Cash	8,000					
Merchandise inventory	9,800					
Prepaid selling expenses	8,000					
Store equipment	40,000					
Accumulated depreciation, store equipment		9,800				
Accounts payable		14,840				
Salaries payable		0				
Eldon Perdu, capital		25,360				
Eldon Perdu, withdrawals	3,600					
Sales		858,000				
Sales returns and allowances	33,000					
Sales discounts	8,000					
Cost of goods sold	431,000					
Sales salaries expense	94,000					
Utilities expense, store	12,600					
Depreciation expense, store equip.	-					
Other selling expenses	70,000					
Other administrative expenses	190,000					
Totals	908,000	908,000				
Profit						
Totals						

(title above table:) **Perdu Sales** / **Work Sheet** / **For Year Ended December 31, 2023**

Copyright © 2022 by McGraw Hill Ltd.

Fundamental Accounting Principles, 17ce, Working Papers

Exercise 5-13 (cont'd.)

Part b

Income Statement			

Analysis component:

_____
_____
_____
_____
_____
_____
_____

Exercise 5-14

1. _____
_____

2. _____
_____

3. _____
_____
_____

*Exercise 5-15

	(a)	(b)	(c)
Purchases			
Purchase discounts			
Purchase returns and allowances			
Transportation-in			
Cost of goods purchased			
Beginning inventory			
Cost of goods purchased			
Ending inventory			
Cost of goods sold			

*Exercise 5-16

	Company A		Company B	
	2023	2022	2023	2022
Sales	110,000	178,000	90,000	
Cost of goods sold:				
Merch. inventory (beginning)	8,700	27,300	8,875	6,000
Net cost of merchandise purchases	82,000			26,100
Merch. Inventory (ending)		(22,000)	(8,920)	(9,875)
Cost of goods sold	82,300	106,000		
Gross profit from sales			39,545	19,775
Operating expenses	26,000	54,000	27,000	
Profit (loss)	1,700	18,000		6,275
Gross profit ratio				

Analysis component:
_____
_____
_____
_____

*Exercise 5-17

	(a)	(b)	(c)
Invoice cost of merch. purchases	44,000	21,000	16,250
Purchase discounts	2,000		325
Purchase returns and allowances	1,500	750	550
Cost of transportation-in		1,750	2,000
Merchandise inventory (beginning)	4,500		3,500
Net cost of merchandise purchases	44,700	19,750	
Merchandise inventory (ending)	2,200	3,750	
Cost of goods sold		20,800	17,065

*Exercise 5-18

a. Periodic System   **GENERAL JOURNAL**   Page____

Date		Account Titles and Explanation	PR	Debit	Credit

*Exercise 5-18 (cont'd.)

b. Perpetual System   **GENERAL JOURNAL**   Page____

Date		Account Titles and Explanation	PR	Debit	Credit

*Exercise 5-19

GENERAL JOURNAL　　　　　Page____

Date	Account Titles and Explanation	PR	Debit	Credit

Name: _____

*Exercise 5-20

GENERAL JOURNAL

Page____

Date	Account Titles and Explanation	PR	Debit	Credit

*Exercise 5-21

GENERAL JOURNAL Page____

Date		Account Titles and Explanation	PR	Debit	Credit

*Exercise 5-22

GENERAL JOURNAL   Page____

Date	Account Titles and Explanation	PR	Debit	Credit

*Exercise 5-23

GENERAL JOURNAL

Page____

Date		Account Titles and Explanation	PR	Debit	Credit

*Exercise 5-23 (concl'd.)

GENERAL JOURNAL   Page____

Date	Account Titles and Explanation	PR	Debit	Credit

Chapter 5

Name: _____

*Exercise 5-24

a. Entries journalized by Wilson Purchasing:

GENERAL JOURNAL   Page____

Date	Account Titles and Explanation	PR	Debit	Credit

b. Entries journalized by Happy Sales:

GENERAL JOURNAL   Page____

Date	Account Titles and Explanation	PR	Debit	Credit

*Exercise 5-25

a.

b.

c.

d. _____

_____

_____

Analysis component:

_____

_____

_____

_____

_____

_____

_____

*Exercise 5-26

a. _____

b. _____

c. _____

Income Statement

Name: _____

*Exercise 5-27

GENERAL JOURNAL   Page____

Date		Account Titles and Explanation	PR	Debit	Credit

*Exercise 5-28

GENERAL JOURNAL   Page____

Date		Account Titles and Explanation	PR	Debit	Credit

*Exercise 5-29

GENERAL JOURNAL

Page_____

Date		Account Titles and Explanation	PR	Debit	Credit

Problem 5-1A

Part 1　　　　　　　　　　GENERAL JOURNAL　　　　　　　Page＿＿

Date	Account Titles and Explanation	PR	Debit	Credit

Problem 5-1A (concl'd.)

GENERAL JOURNAL   Page____

Date		Account Titles and Explanation	PR	Debit	Credit

Part 2

a. _____

b. _____

c. _____

Problem 5-2A

GENERAL JOURNAL   Page____

Date		Account Titles and Explanation	PR	Debit	Credit

Name: _____

Problem 5-2A (cont'd.)

GENERAL JOURNAL

Page____

Date	Account Titles and Explanation	PR	Debit	Credit

Name: _____

Problem 5-2A (cont'd.)

GENERAL JOURNAL

Page____

Date	Account Titles and Explanation	PR	Debit	Credit

Calculations:

Name: _____

Problem 5-2A (concl'd.)

Analysis component:

Email

To: Accounts Payable Department
From: Senior Purchaser, Belton Company

Re: Maximizing purchase discounts
_____

_____
_____
_____
_____
_____
_____
_____
_____
_____
_____
_____
_____
_____
_____
_____
_____
_____
_____
_____
_____
_____
_____
_____
_____

Problem 5-3A

GENERAL JOURNAL

Page____

Date		Account Titles and Explanation	PR	Debit	Credit

Name: _____

Problem 5-3A (concl'd.)

GENERAL JOURNAL

Page____

Date	Account Titles and Explanation	PR	Debit	Credit

GENERAL JOURNAL

Page____

Date		Account Titles and Explanation	PR	Debit	Credit

Name: _____

Problem 5-4A (concl'd.)

Part 2- Multiple-step

Income Statement

Analysis component:

_____

_____

_____

_____

_____

_____

Name: _____

Problem 5-5A

Part 1 - Classified, multiple-step

Income Statement			

Part 2 - Single-step

Income Statement		

Problem 5-6A

a. _____
_____
_____

b. _____
_____
_____

c. _____
_____
_____

	Tank Tops	Pullovers	Yoga Pants
Sale price			
Cost			
Gross Profit			
Gross Profit %			

d. _____
_____
_____
_____

Problem 5-7A

Part 1 – Classified, multiple-step

Income Statement			

Name: _____

Problem 5-7A (concl'd.)

Part 2 – Single-step

Income Statement		

Analysis component:

_____

_____

_____

_____

_____

_____

_____

Name: _____

Problem 5-8A

Part 1 – Classified, multiple-step

Income Statement			

Part 2 – Multiple-step

Income Statement		

Problem 5-8A (concl'd.)

Part 3 – Single-step

	Income Statement		

Analysis component:

_____
_____
_____
_____
_____
_____
_____

*Problem 5-9A

GENERAL JOURNAL

Date	Account Titles and Explanation	PR	Debit	Credit

Name: _____

*Problem 5-10A

GENERAL JOURNAL   Page____

Date	Account Titles and Explanation	PR	Debit	Credit

Name: _____

GENERAL JOURNAL

Page____

Date		Account Titles and Explanation	PR	Debit	Credit

*Problem 5-11A

1. _____
_____
_____
_____
_____
_____
_____

2. _____
_____
_____
_____
_____
_____
_____
_____

3. _____
_____
_____
_____
_____
_____
_____
_____
_____
_____
_____
_____

*Problem 5-11A (concl'd.)

4. Multi-step

Income Statement		

5. Single-step

Income Statement		

*Problem 5-12A

Income Statement				

*Problem 5-13A

GENERAL JOURNAL   Page____

Date	Account Titles and Explanation	PR	Debit	Credit

*Problem 5-14A

GENERAL JOURNAL   Page____

Date	Account Titles and Explanation	PR	Debit	Credit

Name: _____

Problem 5-1B

Part 1   GENERAL JOURNAL   Page____

Date	Account Titles and Explanation	PR	Debit	Credit

Problem 5-1B (concl'd.)

GENERAL JOURNAL   Page____

Date		Account Titles and Explanation	PR	Debit	Credit

Part 2

a. _____

b. _____

c. _____

Problem 5-2B

GENERAL JOURNAL   Page____

Date		Account Titles and Explanation	PR	Debit	Credit

Problem 5-2B (cont'd.)

GENERAL JOURNAL

Date	Account Titles and Explanation	PR	Debit	Credit

Problem 5-2B (concl'd.)

GENERAL JOURNAL

Page____

Date	Account Titles and Explanation	PR	Debit	Credit

Analysis component:

_____
_____
_____
_____
_____
_____
_____
_____
_____
_____
_____
_____
_____
_____

Problem 5-3B

GENERAL JOURNAL

Page____

Date		Account Titles and Explanation	PR	Debit	Credit

Problem 5-3B (concl'd.)

GENERAL JOURNAL　　　　　　　　　　　　　　　Page____

Date	Account Titles and Explanation	PR	Debit	Credit

Analysis component:

_____

_____

_____

_____

_____

Problem 5-4B

Part 1

GENERAL JOURNAL Page____

Date	Account Titles and Explanation	PR	Debit	Credit

Problem 5-4B (concl'd.)

Part 2 – Multiple-step

Income Statement

Analysis component:

_____
_____
_____
_____
_____
_____

Problem 5-5B

1. **Classified, multiple-step**

Income Statement

2. **Single-step**

Income Statement

Name: _____

Problem 5-6B

a. _____
_____
_____

b. _____
_____
_____

c. _____
_____
_____

	Small Handbags	Medium Handbags	Large Handbags
Sale price			
Cost			
Gross Profit			
Gross Profit %			

d. _____
_____
_____
_____
_____
_____
_____
_____
_____
_____

Name: _____

Problem 5-7B

Part 1 – Classified, multiple-step

	Income Statement			

Part 2 – Single-step

	Income Statement		

Analysis component:

_____
_____
_____
_____

Name: _____

Problem 5-8B

Part 1 – Classified, multiple-step

Income Statement			

Problem 5-8B (concl'd.)

Part 2 – Multiple-step

Income Statement			

Part 3 – Single-step

Income Statement			

Name: _____

*Problem 5-9B

GENERAL JOURNAL   Page____

Date	Account Titles and Explanation	PR	Debit	Credit

Name: _____

*Problem 5-10B

GENERAL JOURNAL

Page____

Date	Account Titles and Explanation	PR	Debit	Credit

*Problem 5-10B (concl'd.)

GENERAL JOURNAL

Page____

Date	Account Titles and Explanation	PR	Debit	Credit

Name: _____

*Problem 5-11B

1. _____

2. _____

3. _____

*Problem 5-11B (concl'd.)

4. Multiple-step

Income Statement		

5. Single-step

Income Statement		

*Problem 5-11B (Concluded)

Analysis and calculations:

_____

_____
_____
_____
_____
_____
_____
_____
_____
_____
_____
_____
_____
_____
_____
_____
_____
_____
_____
_____
_____
_____
_____
_____
_____
_____
_____
_____
_____
_____
_____
_____
_____
_____
_____
_____
_____
_____
_____
_____

Name: _____

Income Statement				

Name: _____

*Problem 5-13B

GENERAL JOURNAL

Page____

Date		Account Titles and Explanation	PR	Debit	Credit

*Problem 5-13B (concl'd.)

GENERAL JOURNAL   Page____

Date	Account Titles and Explanation	PR	Debit	Credit

*Problem 5-14B

GENERAL JOURNAL   Page____

Date	Account Titles and Explanation	PR	Debit	Credit

*Problem 5-14B (concl'd.)

GENERAL JOURNAL   Page____

Date		Account Titles and Explanation	PR	Debit	Credit

Cumulative Prob. (Perpetual)

Part 1　　　　　**Echo Systems**

GENERAL JOURNAL　　　　　Page____

Date	Account Titles and Explanation	PR	Debit	Credit

Name: _____

Cumulative Prob. (Perpetual)

Part 1   **Echo Systems (cont'd.)**

GENERAL JOURNAL

Page_____

Date	Account Titles and Explanation	PR	Debit	Credit

Cumulative Prob. (Perpetual)

Part 1   Echo Systems (cont'd.)

GENERAL JOURNAL   Page____

Date		Account Titles and Explanation	PR	Debit	Credit

Cumulative Prob. (Perpetual)

Part 1 Echo Systems (cont'd.)

GENERAL JOURNAL

Page____

Date	Account Titles and Explanation	PR	Debit	Credit

Cumulative Prob. (Perpetual)

Part 2   Echo Systems (cont'd.)

GENERAL LEDGER

Cash   ACCOUNT NO. 101

DATE	EXPLANATION	PR	DEBIT	CREDIT	BALANCE
2023 Dec. 31	Beginning Balance				89,090

Cumulative Prob. (Perpetual)

Part 2   **Echo Systems (cont'd.)**

Accounts Receivable – Alamo Engineering   ACCOUNT NO. 106.1

DATE	EXPLANATION	PR	DEBIT	CREDIT	BALANCE
2023 Dec. 31	Beginning Balance				-0-

Accounts Receivable – Buckman Services   ACCOUNT NO. 106.2

DATE	EXPLANATION	PR	DEBIT	CREDIT	BALANCE
2023 Dec. 31	Beginning Balance				-0-

Accounts Receivable – Capital Leasing   ACCOUNT NO. 106.3

DATE	EXPLANATION	PR	DEBIT	CREDIT	BALANCE
2023 Dec. 31	Beginning Balance				-0-

Accounts Receivable – Decker Co.   ACCOUNT NO. 106.4

DATE	EXPLANATION	PR	DEBIT	CREDIT	BALANCE
2023 Dec. 31	Beginning Balance				2,700

Accounts Receivable – Elite Corporation   ACCOUNT NO. 106.5

DATE	EXPLANATION	PR	DEBIT	CREDIT	BALANCE
2023 Dec. 31	Beginning Balance				-0-

Cumulative Prob. (Perpetual)

Part 2   Echo Systems (cont'd.)

Accounts Receivable – Fostek Co.   ACCOUNT NO. 106.6

DATE	EXPLANATION	PR	DEBIT	CREDIT	BALANCE
2023 Dec. 31	Beginning Balance				3,000

Accounts Receivable – Grandview Co.   ACCOUNT NO. 106.7

DATE	EXPLANATION	PR	DEBIT	CREDIT	BALANCE
2023 Dec. 31	Beginning Balance				-0-

Accounts Receivable – Hacienda, Inc.   ACCOUNT NO. 106.8

DATE	EXPLANATION	PR	DEBIT	CREDIT	BALANCE
2023 Dec. 31	Beginning Balance				-0-

Accounts Receivable – Images, Inc.   ACCOUNT NO. 106.9

DATE	EXPLANATION	PR	DEBIT	CREDIT	BALANCE
2023 Dec. 31	Beginning Balance				-0-

Cumulative Prob. (Perpetual)

Part 2   **Echo Systems (cont'd.)**

Merchandise Inventory — ACCOUNT NO. 119

DATE	EXPLANATION	PR	DEBIT	CREDIT	BALANCE

Computer Supplies — ACCOUNT NO. 126

DATE	EXPLANATION	PR	DEBIT	CREDIT	BALANCE
2023 Dec. 31	Balance				1,440

Prepaid Insurance — ACCOUNT NO. 128

DATE	EXPLANATION	PR	DEBIT	CREDIT	BALANCE
2023 Dec. 31	Beginning Balance				3,240

Prepaid Rent — ACCOUNT NO. 131

DATE	EXPLANATION	PR	DEBIT	CREDIT	BALANCE
2023 Dec. 31	Beginning Balance				2,250

Office Equipment — ACCOUNT NO. 163

DATE	EXPLANATION	PR	DEBIT	CREDIT	BALANCE
2023 Dec. 31	Beginning Balance				18,000

Cumulative Prob. (Perpetual)

Part 2   Echo Systems (cont'd.)

Accumulated Depreciation, Office Equipment — ACCOUNT NO. 164

DATE	EXPLANATION	PR	DEBIT	CREDIT	BALANCE
2023 Dec. 31	Beginning Balance				1,500

Computer Equipment — ACCOUNT NO. 167

DATE	EXPLANATION	PR	DEBIT	CREDIT	BALANCE
2023 Dec. 31	Beginning Balance				36,000

Accumulated Depreciation, Computer Equipment — ACCOUNT NO. 168

DATE	EXPLANATION	PR	DEBIT	CREDIT	BALANCE
2023 Dec. 31	Beginning Balance				2,250

Accounts Payable — ACCOUNT NO. 201

DATE	EXPLANATION	PR	DEBIT	CREDIT	BALANCE
2023 Dec. 31	Beginning Balance				2,310

Wages Payable — ACCOUNT NO. 210

DATE	EXPLANATION	PR	DEBIT	CREDIT	BALANCE
2023 Dec. 31	Beginning Balance				800

Cumulative Prob. (Perpetual)

Part 2   **Echo Systems (cont'd.)**

Unearned Computer Services Revenue   ACCOUNT NO. 236

DATE	EXPLANATION	PR	DEBIT	CREDIT	BALANCE
2023 Dec. 31	Beginning Balance				3,000

Mary Graham, Capital   ACCOUNT NO. 301

DATE	EXPLANATION	PR	DEBIT	CREDIT	BALANCE
2023 Dec. 31	Beginning Balance				145,860

Mary Graham, Withdrawals   ACCOUNT NO. 302

DATE	EXPLANATION	PR	DEBIT	CREDIT	BALANCE

Computer Services Revenue   ACCOUNT NO. 403

DATE	EXPLANATION	PR	DEBIT	CREDIT	BALANCE

Sales   ACCOUNT NO. 413

DATE	EXPLANATION	PR	DEBIT	CREDIT	BALANCE

Cumulative Prob. (Perpetual)

Part 2   Echo Systems (cont'd.)

Sales Discounts — ACCOUNT NO. 414

DATE	EXPLANATION	PR	DEBIT	CREDIT	BALANCE

Sales Returns and Allowances — ACCOUNT NO. 415

DATE	EXPLANATION	PR	DEBIT	CREDIT	BALANCE

Cost of Goods Sold — ACCOUNT NO. 502

DATE	EXPLANATION	PR	DEBIT	CREDIT	BALANCE

Depreciation Expense, Office Equipment — ACCOUNT NO. 612

DATE	EXPLANATION	PR	DEBIT	CREDIT	BALANCE

Depreciation Expense, Computer Equipment — ACCOUNT NO. 613

DATE	EXPLANATION	PR	DEBIT	CREDIT	BALANCE

Wages Expense — ACCOUNT NO. 623

DATE	EXPLANATION	PR	DEBIT	CREDIT	BALANCE

Chapter 5

Name: _____

Cumulative Prob. (Perpetual)

Part 2   Echo Systems (cont'd.)

Insurance Expense   ACCOUNT NO. 637

DATE	EXPLANATION	PR	DEBIT	CREDIT	BALANCE

Rent Expense   ACCOUNT NO. 640

DATE	EXPLANATION	PR	DEBIT	CREDIT	BALANCE

Computer Supplies Expense   ACCOUNT NO. 652

DATE	EXPLANATION	P.R.	DEBIT	CREDIT	BALANCE

Advertising Expense   ACCOUNT NO. 655

DATE	EXPLANATION	PR	DEBIT	CREDIT	BALANCE

Mileage Expense   ACCOUNT NO. 676

DATE	EXPLANATION	PR	DEBIT	CREDIT	BALANCE

Repairs Expense, Computer   ACCOUNT NO. 684

DATE	EXPLANATION	PR	DEBIT	CREDIT	BALANCE

Charitable Donations Expense   ACCOUNT NO. 699

DATE	EXPLANATION	PR	DEBIT	CREDIT	BALANCE

Cumulative Prob. (Perpetual)

Part 3   **Echo Systems**

ECHO SYSTEMS
Partial Work Sheet
For Three Months Ended March 31, 2024

Acct. No.	Account Title	Unadjusted Trial Balance Dr.	Cr.	Adjustments Dr.	Cr.	Adjusted Trial Balance Dr.	Cr.
101	Cash						
106.1	Alamo Engineering Co.						
106.2	Buckman Services						
106.3	Capital Leasing						
106.4	Decker Co.						
106.5	Elite Corporation						
106.6	Fostek Co.						
106.7	Grandview Co.						
106.8	Hacienda Inc.						
106.9	Images Inc.						
119	Merchandise inventory						
126	Computer supplies						
128	Prepaid insurance						
131	Prepaid rent						
163	Office equipment						
164	Accum. deprec., office equipment						
167	Computer equipment						
168	Accum. deprec., computer equip.						
201	Accounts payable						
210	Wages payable						
236	Unearned computer services rev.						
301	Mary Graham, capital						
302	Mary Graham, withdrawals						
403	Computer services revenue						
413	Sales						
414	Sales discounts						
415	Sales returns and allowances						
502	Cost of goods sold						
612	Deprec. exp., office equipment						
613	Deprec. exp., computer equip.						
623	Wages expense						
637	Insurance expense						
640	Rent expense						
652	Computer supplies expense						
655	Advertising expense						
676	Mileage expense						
684	Repairs expense, computer						
699	Charitable donations expense						
	Totals						

Name: _____

Cumulative Prob. (Perpetual)

Part 4   Echo Systems (cont'd.)

ECHO SYSTEMS
Income Statement
For Three Months Ended March 31, 2024

Part 5

ECHO SYSTEMS
Statement of Changes in Equity
For Three Months Ended March 31, 2024

Cumulative Prob. (Perpetual)

Part 6   **Echo Systems (concl'd.)**

ECHO SYSTEMS
Balance Sheet
March 31, 2024

Cumulative Prob. (Periodic)

Part 1   **Echo Systems**

Journal Entries

GENERAL JOURNAL   Page____

Date	Account Titles and Explanation	PR	Debit	Credit

Cumulative Prob. (Periodic)

Part 1   Echo Systems (cont'd.)

Date		Account Titles and Explanation	PR	Debit	Credit

Cumulative Prob. (Periodic)

Part 1   Echo Systems (cont'd.)

Date	Account Titles and Explanation	PR	Debit	Credit

Cumulative Prob. (Periodic)

Part 1   Echo Systems (cont'd.)

Date	Account Titles and Explanation	PR	Debit	Credit

Copyright © 2022 by McGraw Hill Ltd.
Fundamental Accounting Principles, 17ce, Working Papers

Name: _____

Cumulative Prob. (Periodic)

Part 2   Echo Systems (cont'd.)

GENERAL LEDGER

Cash					ACCOUNT NO. 101

DATE	EXPLANATION	PR	DEBIT	CREDIT	BALANCE
2023 Dec. 31	Beginning Balance				89,090

Cumulative Prob. (Periodic)

Part 2   Echo Systems (cont'd.)

Accounts Receivable – Alamo Engineering   ACCOUNT NO. 106.1

DATE	EXPLANATION	PR	DEBIT	CREDIT	BALANCE
2023 Dec. 31	Beginning Balance				-0-

Accounts Receivable – Buckman Services   ACCOUNT NO. 106.2

DATE	EXPLANATION	PR	DEBIT	CREDIT	BALANCE
2023 Dec. 31	Beginning Balance				-0-

Accounts Receivable – Capital Leasing   ACCOUNT NO. 106.3

DATE	EXPLANATION	PR	DEBIT	CREDIT	BALANCE
2023 Dec. 31	Beginning Balance				-0-

Accounts Receivable – Decker Co.   ACCOUNT NO. 106.4

DATE	EXPLANATION	PR	DEBIT	CREDIT	BALANCE
2023 Dec. 31	Beginning Balance				2,700

Accounts Receivable – Elite Corporation   ACCOUNT NO. 106.5

DATE	EXPLANATION	PR	DEBIT	CREDIT	BALANCE
2023 Dec. 31	Beginning Balance				-0-

Cumulative Prob. (Periodic)

Part 2   **Echo Systems (cont'd.)**

Accounts Receivable – Fostek Co.   ACCOUNT NO. 106.6

DATE	EXPLANATION	PR	DEBIT	CREDIT	BALANCE
2023 Dec. 31	Beginning Balance				3,000

Accounts Receivable – Grandview Co.   ACCOUNT NO. 106.7

DATE	EXPLANATION	PR	DEBIT	CREDIT	BALANCE
2023 Dec. 31	Beginning Balance				-0-

Accounts Receivable – Hacienda Inc.   ACCOUNT NO. 106.8

DATE	EXPLANATION	PR	DEBIT	CREDIT	BALANCE
2023 Dec. 31	Beginning Balance				-0-

Accounts Receivable – Images Inc.   ACCOUNT NO. 106.9

DATE	EXPLANATION	PR	DEBIT	CREDIT	BALANCE
2023 Dec. 31	Beginning Balance				-0-

Merchandise Inventory   ACCOUNT NO. 119

DATE	EXPLANATION	PR	DEBIT	CREDIT	BALANCE
2023 Dec. 31	Beginning Balance				-0-

Computer Supplies   ACCOUNT NO. 126

DATE	EXPLANATION	PR	DEBIT	CREDIT	BALANCE
2023 Dec. 31	Beginning Balance				1,440

Cumulative Prob. (Periodic)

Part 2   Echo Systems (cont'd.)

Prepaid Insurance   ACCOUNT NO. 128

DATE	EXPLANATION	PR	DEBIT	CREDIT	BALANCE
2023 Dec. 31	Beginning Balance				3,240

Prepaid Rent   ACCOUNT NO. 131

DATE	EXPLANATION	PR	DEBIT	CREDIT	BALANCE
2023 Dec. 31	Beginning Balance				2,250

Office Equipment   ACCOUNT NO. 163

DATE	EXPLANATION	PR	DEBIT	CREDIT	BALANCE
2023 Dec. 31	Beginning Balance				18,000

Accumulated Depreciation, Office Equipment   ACCOUNT NO. 164

DATE	EXPLANATION	PR	DEBIT	CREDIT	BALANCE
2023 Dec. 31	Beginning Balance				1,500

Computer Equipment   ACCOUNT NO. 167

DATE	EXPLANATION	PR	DEBIT	CREDIT	BALANCE
2023 Dec. 31	Beginning Balance				36,000

Accumulated Depreciation, Computer Equipment   ACCOUNT NO. 168

DATE	EXPLANATION	PR	DEBIT	CREDIT	BALANCE
2023 Dec. 31	Beginning Balance				2,250

Name: _____

Cumulative Prob. (Periodic)

Part 2   Echo Systems (cont'd.)

Accounts Payable   ACCOUNT NO. 201

DATE	EXPLANATION	PR	DEBIT	CREDIT	BALANCE
2023 Dec. 31	Beginning Balance				2,310

Wages Payable   ACCOUNT NO. 210

DATE	EXPLANATION	PR	DEBIT	CREDIT	BALANCE
2023 Dec. 31	Beginning Balance				800

Unearned Computer Services Revenue   ACCOUNT NO. 236

DATE	EXPLANATION	PR	DEBIT	CREDIT	BALANCE
2023 Dec. 31	Beginning Balance				3,000

Mary Graham, Capital   ACCOUNT NO. 301

DATE	EXPLANATION	PR	DEBIT	CREDIT	BALANCE
2023 Dec. 31	Beginning Balance				145,860

Mary Graham, Withdrawals   ACCOUNT NO. 302

DATE	EXPLANATION	PR	DEBIT	CREDIT	BALANCE

Cumulative Prob. (Periodic)

Part 2   Echo Systems (cont'd.)

Computer Services Revenue   ACCOUNT NO. 403

DATE	EXPLANATION	PR	DEBIT	CREDIT	BALANCE

Sales   ACCOUNT NO. 413

DATE	EXPLANATION	PR	DEBIT	CREDIT	BALANCE

Sales Discounts   ACCOUNT NO. 414

DATE	EXPLANATION	PR	DEBIT	CREDIT	BALANCE

Sales Returns and Allowances   ACCOUNT NO. 415

DATE	EXPLANATION	PR	DEBIT	CREDIT	BALANCE

Purchases   ACCOUNT NO. 505

DATE	EXPLANATION	PR	DEBIT	CREDIT	BALANCE

Purchase Returns and Allowances   ACCOUNT NO. 506

DATE	EXPLANATION	PR	DEBIT	CREDIT	BALANCE

Purchase Discounts   ACCOUNT NO. 507

DATE	EXPLANATION	PR	DEBIT	CREDIT	BALANCE

Transportation-In   ACCOUNT NO. 508

DATE	EXPLANATION	PR	DEBIT	CREDIT	BALANCE

Depreciation Expense, Office Equipment   ACCOUNT NO. 612

DATE	EXPLANATION	PR	DEBIT	CREDIT	BALANCE

Depreciation Expense, Computer Equipment   ACCOUNT NO. 613

DATE	EXPLANATION	PR	DEBIT	CREDIT	BALANCE

Wages Expense   ACCOUNT NO. 623

DATE	EXPLANATION	PR	DEBIT	CREDIT	BALANCE

Cumulative Prob. (Periodic)

Part 2   Echo Systems (cont'd.)

Insurance Expense — ACCOUNT NO. 637

DATE	EXPLANATION	PR	DEBIT	CREDIT	BALANCE

Rent Expense — ACCOUNT NO. 640

DATE	EXPLANATION	PR	DEBIT	CREDIT	BALANCE

Computer Supplies Expense — ACCOUNT NO. 652

DATE	EXPLANATION	PR	DEBIT	CREDIT	BALANCE

Advertising Expense — ACCOUNT NO. 655

DATE	EXPLANATION	PR	DEBIT	CREDIT	BALANCE

Mileage Expense — ACCOUNT NO. 676

DATE	EXPLANATION	PR	DEBIT	CREDIT	BALANCE

Repairs Expense, Computer — ACCOUNT NO. 684

DATE	EXPLANATION	PR	DEBIT	CREDIT	BALANCE

Charitable Donations Expense — ACCOUNT NO. 699

DATE	EXPLANATION	PR	DEBIT	CREDIT	BALANCE

Cumulative Prob. (Periodic)

Part 3　　　　　　　**Echo Systems (concl'd.)**

ECHO SYSTEMS
Partial Work Sheet
March 31, 2024

Acct. No.	Account Title	Unadjusted Trial Balance		Adjustments		Adjusted Trial Balance	
		Debit	Credit	Debit	Credit	Debit	Credit
101	Cash						
106.1	Alamo Engineering Co.						
106.2	Buckman Services						
106.3	Capital Leasing						
106.4	Decker Co.						
106.5	Elite Corporation						
106.6	Fostek Co.						
106.7	Grandview Co.						
106.8	Hacienda Inc.						
106.9	Images Inc.						
119	Merchandise inventory						
126	Computer supplies						
128	Prepaid insurance						
131	Prepaid rent						
163	Office equipment						
164	Accum. deprec., office equipment						
167	Computer equipment						
168	Accum. deprec., computer equip.						
201	Accounts payable						
210	Wages payable						
236	Unearned computer services rev.						
301	Mary Graham, capital						
302	Mary Graham, withdrawals						
403	Computer services revenue						
413	Sales						
414	Sales discounts						
415	Sales returns and allowances						
505	Purchases						
506	Purchase returns and allowances						
507	Purchase discounts						
508	Transportation-in						
612	Deprec. exp., office equipment						
613	Deprec. exp., computer equip.						
623	Wages expense						
637	Insurance expense						
640	Rent expense						
652	Computer supplies expense						
655	Advertising expense						
676	Mileage expense						
684	Repairs expense, computer						
699	Charitable donations expense						
	Totals						

Parts 4, 5, and 6: Use the forms provided earlier.

Quick Study 6-1

_____
_____
_____
_____
_____
_____
_____
_____
_____
_____
_____

Quick Study 6-2
FIFO - Perpetual

Date	Goods Purchased	Cost of Goods Sold	Inventory Balance

*Quick Study 6-3
Weighted Average - Periodic

Date	Goods Purchased	Cost of Goods Sold	Inventory Balance

*Quick Study 6-4
FIFO – Periodic

		Ending Inventory	Cost of Goods Sold

*Quick Study 6-5
Weighted Average – Periodic

	Ending Inventory	Cost of Goods Sold

*Quick Study 6-6
FIFO - Periodic

Date	Goods Purchased	Cost of Goods Sold	Inventory Balance

Quick Study 6-7
Weighted Average - Perpetual

Date	Goods Purchased	Cost of Goods Sold	Inventory Balance

Quick Study 6-8
Specific Identification - Perpetual

***Quick Study 6-9**

FIFO – Periodic

	Ending Inventory	Cost of Goods Sold

***Quick Study 6-10**
Weighted Average – Periodic

	Ending Inventory	Cost of Goods Sold

***Quick Study 6-11**
Specific Identification – Periodic

	Ending Inventory	Cost of Goods Sold

Quick Study 6-12

Inventory Items	Units on Hand	Per Unit Cost	Per Unit NRV	Total Cost	Total NRV	LCM-Items
Mountain Bikes	11	$600	$550			
Skateboards	13	350	425			
Gliders	26	800	700			

LCM applied to each product .... $ _____

Name: _____

Quick Study 6-13

Inventory Turnover

_____
_____
_____

Days' sales in inventory

_____
_____
_____
_____

Quick Study 6-14

_____
_____
_____
_____
_____
_____
_____
_____

Quick Study 6-15

1. _____
_____
_____

2. _____
_____
_____

Quick Study 6-16

_____
_____
_____

Name: _____

Quick Study 6-17

_____
_____
_____
_____
_____
_____
_____
_____
_____
_____

Quick Study 6-18

_____
_____
_____
_____
_____
_____
_____
_____
_____
_____
_____

Quick Study 6-19

_____
_____
_____
_____
_____
_____
_____
_____
_____
_____
_____
_____
_____
_____

Name: _____

Quick Study 6-20

a. FIFO Perpetual

Date	Purchases	Sales (at cost)	Inventory Balance

b. Moving Weighted Average Perpetual

Date	Purchases	Sales (at cost)	Inventory Balance

Quick Study 6-21

Specific identification inventory method

Date	Purchases	Sales (at cost)	Inventory Balance

Quick Study 6-22

Date	Purchases/ Transportation-In/ (Purchase Returns/Discounts) Units	Cost Per Unit	Total $	Cost of Goods Sold/ (Returns to Inventory) Units	Cost Per Unit	Total $	Balance in Inventory Units	Avg Cost Per Unit	Total $
Jan. 1		BFWD					10	$15.00	$150.00
3				6					
7	25	$18.50	$462.50						
8			50.00						
17			(46.25)						
18				14					

Calculations:

_____
_____
_____
_____
_____
_____
_____
_____

Quick Study 6-23

a. _____
b. _____
c. _____

Quick Study 6-24

Parts a and b

Inventory Items	Units on Hand	Per Unit		Total Cost	Total NRV	LCNRV applied to:	
		Cost	NRV			a. Inventory as a Group	b. Each Product
Aprons	9	$6.00	$5.50				
Bottles	12	3.50	4.25				
Candles	25	8.00	7.00				

Part c

GENERAL JOURNAL   Page____

Date		Account Titles and Explanation	PR	Debit	Credit

Quick Study 6-25

a. _____
b. _____
c. _____
d. _____
e. _____
f. _____

Quick Study 6-26

Name: _____

Quick Study 6-27

a. _____

_____

_____

_____

_____

_____

_____

_____

_____

_____

b. _____

_____

Quick Study 6-28

_____

_____

_____

_____

_____

_____

_____

_____

_____

_____

_____

Quick Study 6-29

_____

_____

_____

_____

_____

_____

_____

_____

_____

_____

_____

_____

Fundamental Accounting Principles, 17ce, Working Papers

Name: _____

Quick Study 6-30

_____
_____
_____
_____
_____
_____
_____
_____
_____

Quick Study 6-31

a. Days' sales in inventory:

_____
_____
_____
_____
_____
_____
_____
_____
_____

b. Inventory turnover:

_____
_____
_____
_____
_____
_____
_____
_____
_____

*Quick Study 6-32

a. _____
_____
_____

b. _____
_____
_____

Chapter 6

Name: _____

Exercise 6-1

	Include / Exclude?	Explanation and if applicable, correct inventory cost
a.		
b.		
c.		
d.		

Exercise 6-2

a. FIFO Perpetual

Date	Purchases	Sales (at cost)	Inventory Balance

Exercise 6-2 (cont'd.)

Gross profit calculation under FIFO:

_____
_____
_____
_____
_____
_____

b. Moving Weighted Average Perpetual

Date	Purchases	Sales (at cost)	Inventory Balance

Gross profit calculation under Moving Weighted Average:

_____
_____
_____
_____
_____

Name: _____

Exercise 6-3

Specific Identification

Date	Purchases	Sales (at cost)	Inventory Balance

Gross profit calculation under Specific Identification:

Exercise 6-4

1. FIFO Perpetual

Date	Purchases	Sales (at cost)	Inventory Balance

2. Moving Weighted Average Perpetual

Date	Purchases	Sales (at cost)	Inventory Balance

Exercise 6-5

1.
_____
_____
_____
_____
_____
_____
_____

2.
_____
_____
_____
_____
_____
_____
_____

3(a). FIFO Perpetual

Date	Purchases	Sales (at cost)	Inventory Balance

Exercise 6-5 (concl'd.)

3(b). Moving Weighted Average Perpetual

Date	Purchases	Sales (at cost)	Inventory Balance

Exercise 6-6

Specific Identification

Date	Purchases	Sales (at cost)	Inventory Balance

Exercise 6-7

	Car Armour			
	Income Statements			
	For the Year Ended December 31, 2023			
	FIFO	**Moving Weighted Average**	**Specific Identification**	

1. _____

_____

2. _____

_____

Name: _____

Exercise 6-8

1.

July 1	21 units	@	$46	=	
July 3	66 units	@	51	=	
July 6	116 units	@	56	=	
July 23	<u>62 units</u>	@	56	=	
Totals	<u> units </u>				

      available for   **cost of goods**
      sale   **available for sale**

2.
Units sold:
    July 17   61 units
    July 31   <u>152 units</u>
      Totals   <u>   units </u>

Therefore, units remaining in ending inventory:
        _____units available for sale
        _____units sold
        _____units remaining in ending inventory

Exercise 6-8 (continued)

3a. FIFO

Date	Purchases			Sales (at cost)			Inventory Balance		
	Units	Unit Cost	Total Cost	Units	Unit Cost	Cost of Goods Sold	Units	Cost	Total Cc
July 1	21 @	$46							
July 3	66 @	$51							
July 6	116 @	$56							
July 17									
July 23	62 @	$56							
July 31									
Total									
	Cost of goods available for sale =			Cost of goods sold +			Ending inventory		

Exercise 6-8 (continued)

3b. Moving Weighted Average

Date	Purchases			Sales (at cost)			Inventory Balance		
	Units	Unit Cost	Total Cost	Units	Unit Cost	Cost of Goods Sold	Units	Cost	Total Cost
July 1	21 @	$46							
July 3	66 @	$51							
July 6	116 @	$56							
July 17									
July 23	62 @	$56							
July 31									
Total									
	Cost of goods available for sale =			*Cost of goods sold*		+	*Ending inventory*		

Exercise 6-9

Date	Purchases/ Transportation-In/ (Purchase Returns/Discounts) Units	Cost Per Unit	Total $	Cost of Goods Sold/ (Returns to Inventory) Units	Cost Per Unit	Total $	Balance in Inventory Units	Avg Cost Per Unit	Total $
Mar. 1		BFWD					60	$94.00	$5,640.00
2	35	$96.00							
3				22					.
4				(2)					
7				65					
17	40	97.00							
28				43					
Totals									

Calculations:

_____
_____
_____
_____
_____

Analysis component:

_____
_____
_____

Exercise 6-10

Parts a and b

Inventory Items	Units on Hand	Per Unit Cost	NRV	Total Cost	Total NRV	LCNRV applied to: a. Inventory as a Group	b. Each Product
BB	27	$115	$120				
FM	10	150	143				
MB	41	191	177				
SL	45	83	97				

Part c

GENERAL JOURNAL   Page____

Date	Account Titles and Explanation	PR	Debit	Credit

Name: _____

Exercise 6-11

1. _____

_____

_____

_____

2.

For years ended December 31, 2023, 2024, and 2025 Income statement information should have been reported as:			Income statement information actually reported for years ended December 31,					
			2023			2024		2025
Sales								
Cost of goods sold:								
Beginning inventory								
+ Purchases								
– Ending inventory								
= Cost of goods sold								
Gross profit								

Exercise 6-12

_____
_____
_____
_____
_____
_____
_____
_____
_____
_____
_____
_____

Exercise 6-13

	At Cost	*At Retail*

Exercise 6-14

a. Estimated cost of physical inventory:

_____
_____

b. Shrinkage at cost and at retail:	**At Cost**	**At Retail**

Chapter 6   Name: _____

Exercise 6-15

Inventory turnover (2024):
_____
_____
_____
_____

Inventory turnover (2023):
_____
_____
_____
_____

Days' sales in inventory (2024):
_____
_____
_____
_____

Days' sales in inventory (2023):
_____
_____
_____
_____

Comment on Russo's efficiency in using its assets to support increasing sales from 2023 to 2024.
_____
_____
_____
_____

Exercise 6-16

Inventory Items	Units on Hand	Per Unit		Total Cost	Total NRV	LCNRV applied to: Each Product
		Cost	NRV			
Helmets	24	$50	$54			
Bats	17	78	72			
Shoes	38	95	91			
Uniforms	42	36	36			

Exercise 6-17

Year 2 Inventory turnover   **Year 2 Days' Sales in Inventory**

_____   _____

_____   _____

Year 3 Inventory turnover   **Year 3 Days' Sales in Inventory**

_____   _____

_____   _____

Analysis Comment: _____

_____

_____

_____

Name: _____

Exercise 6-18

_____
_____
_____
_____
_____
_____
_____
_____
_____
_____
_____
_____

Exercise 6-19

_____
_____
_____
_____
_____
_____
_____
_____
_____
_____
_____
_____
_____
_____

Name: _____

*Exercise 6-20

	Ending Inventory	Cost of Goods Sold

a. FIFO Periodic:

_____
_____
_____
_____
_____
_____

b. Weighted Average Cost Periodic:

_____
_____
_____
_____
_____
_____

Which method provides the lower profit and why?

_____
_____
_____

*Exercise 6-21

	Ending Inventory	Cost of Goods Sold

a. FIFO Periodic:

_____
_____
_____
_____
_____

b. Weighted Average Cost Periodic:

_____
_____
_____
_____
_____
_____

Which method provides the lower profit and why?

_____
_____
_____

Name: _____

*Exercise 6-22

Ending Inventory: _____
_____
_____
_____
_____
_____
_____

Cost of goods sold: _____
_____
_____
_____
_____
_____
_____

Problem 6-1A

Part 1

	Include / Exclude?	Explanation and if applicable, inventory cost.
a.		
b.		
c.		
d.		
e.		

Part 2

Merchandise Inventory

Unadjusted Balance.	
Adjusted Bal.	

Problem 6-2A

1a. FIFO Perpetual

Date	Purchases	Sales (at cost)	Inventory Balance

Problem 6-2A (cont'd.)

1b. Moving Weighted Average Perpetual

Date	Purchases	Sales (at cost)	Inventory Balance

Problem 6-2A (cont'd.)

2. Specific Identification

Date	Purchases	Sales (at cost)	Inventory Balance

3.   **GENERAL JOURNAL**   Page____

Date	Account Titles and Explanation	PR	Debit	Credit
a.				
b.				

Name: _____

Problem 6-2A (concl'd.)

GENERAL JOURNAL   Page____

Date	Account Titles and Explanation	PR	Debit	Credit
c.				

Name: _____

*Problem 6-3A

a. FIFO PERIODIC basis:

_____
_____
_____
_____
_____
_____
_____

b. Weighted Average PERIODIC basis:

_____
_____
_____
_____
_____
_____
_____
_____

Problem 6-4A

Calculation of cost of goods available for sale and units available for sale:

_____
_____
_____
_____
_____
_____
_____
_____
_____
_____

Calculation of units in ending inventory:

_____
_____
_____
_____
_____
_____

Problem6-4A (cont'd.)

1a. FIFO Perpetual

Date	Purchases	Sales (at cost)	Inventory Balance

1b. Moving Weighted Average Perpetual

Date	Purchases	Sales (at cost)	Inventory Balance

Problem 6-4A (concl'd.)

2.

	FIFO	**Moving Weighted Average**
Sales		
Cost of goods sold....................		
Gross profit............................		

Analysis component: _____

_____

_____

_____

_____

_____

*Problem 6-5A

a. FIFO Periodic:

_____

_____

_____

_____

_____

_____

_____

_____

_____

_____

_____

_____

_____

b. Moving Weighted Average Periodic:

_____

_____

_____

_____

_____

_____

_____

_____

_____

_____

Name: _____

Problem 6-6A

1a. FIFO Perpetual

Date	Purchases	Sales (at cost)	Inventory Balance

Problem 6-6A (cont'd)

1b. Moving Weighted Average Perpetual

Date	Purchases	Sales (at cost)	Inventory Balance

Part 2

	FIFO	Weighted moving average
Sales		
Cost of goods sold		
Gross Profit		

Part 3

_____
_____
_____
_____
_____
_____

Part 4

_____
_____
_____
_____

Problem 6-7A

1a. FIFO Perpetual

Date	Purchases			Sales (at cost)			Inventory Balance		
	Units	Unit Cost	Total Cost	Units	Unit Cost	Cost of Goods Sold	Units	Unit Cost	
Jan. 1	Beginning inventory 295 @ $83.00 =								
Mar. 10	210 @ $87.00 =								
20									
May 13	277 @ $81.00 =								
Aug. 5	260 @ $67.00 =								
Sept 10									
Total									

Cost of goods available for sale = Cost of goods sold   +   Ending invent

Problem 6-7A (cont'd)

1b. Moving Weighted Average Perpetual

te	Purchases			Sales (at cost)			Inventory Balance		
	Units	Unit Cost	Total Cost	Units	Unit Cost	Cost of Goods Sold	Units	Unit Cost	*Total Cost*
1	Beginning inventory 295 @ $83.00 =								
10	210 @ $87.00 =								
20									
13	277 @ $81.00 =								
5	260 @ $67.00 =								
10									
al									

Part 2

	FIFO	Weighted moving average
Sales		
<u>Cost of goods sold</u>		
Gross Profit		

Analysis component:

_____
_____
_____
_____
_____
_____
_____

Problem 6-8A

Fresh Express Company
Income Statement Comparing FIFO and Moving Weighted Average Cost
For Year Ended December 31, 2023

	FIFO	Moving Weighted Average
Sales		
Cost of goods sold		
Gross profit		
Operating expenses		
Profit		

Supporting calculations:

_____
_____
_____
_____
_____
_____
_____
_____
_____
_____
_____
_____
_____
_____

Name: _____

Problem 6-8A (cont'd.)

a. FIFO Perpetual

Date	Purchases	Sales (at cost)	Inventory Balance

b. Moving Weighted Average Perpetual

Date	Purchases	Sales (at cost)	Inventory Balance

Problem 6-8A (concl'd.)

Analysis component:

_____
_____
_____
_____
_____
_____
_____
_____

*Problem 6-9A

Fresh Express Company Income Statement Comparing FIFO and Weighted Average Periodic For Year Ended December 31, 2023		
	FIFO	**Weighted Average**
Sales		
Cost of goods sold		
Gross profit		
Operating expenses		
Profit		

Supporting calculations:

_____
_____
_____
_____
_____
_____
_____
_____
_____
_____
_____
_____
_____
_____
_____

Problem 6-10A

Part 1

a. Cost of Goods Sold:	2023	2024	2025
Reported..	_____	_____	_____
Adjustments: 12/31/2023 error	_____	_____	_____
12/31/2024 error	_____	_____	_____
Corrected...	_____	_____	_____

b. Profit:	2023	2024	2025
Reported..	_____	_____	_____
Adjustments: 12/31/2023 error	_____	_____	_____
12/31/2024 error	_____	_____	_____
Corrected...	_____	_____	_____

c. Total Current Assets:	2023	2024	2025
Reported..	_____	_____	_____
Adjustments: 12/31/2023 error	_____	_____	_____
12/31/2024 error	_____	_____	_____
Corrected...	_____	_____	_____

d. Equity:	2023	2024	2025
Reported..	_____	_____	_____
Adjustments: 12/31/2023 error	_____	_____	_____
12/31/2024 error	_____	_____	_____
Corrected...	_____	_____	_____

Analysis component:

_____
_____
_____
_____
_____
_____
_____
_____
_____
_____
_____
_____
_____
_____
_____

Problem 6-11A

	2023	2024	2025
Corrected Ending Inventory			
Corrected Cost of Goods Sold			
Corrected Profit			

Fundamental Accounting Principles, 17ce, Working Papers

Problem 6-12A

Part 1

| Inventory Items | Units on Hand | Per Unit | | Total Cost | Total NRV | LCNRV applied to: | |
		Cost	NRV			a. Major Group	b. Separately to Each Product
Audio equipment:							
Wireless audio receivers	332	$199	$188				
Touchscreen MP3 players	247	203	223				
Audio mixers	313	193	177				
Audio stands	191	85	103				
Subtotal							
Video:							
Televisions	467	253	298				
5GB video cards	278	171	183				
Satellite video recorders	199	613	618				
Subtotal							
Car Equipment:							
GPS navigators	172	171	145				
Double-DIN Car Deck with iPod/iPhone Control and Aux Input	157	213	198				
Subtotal							
Totals							

2a. **GENERAL JOURNAL** Page____

Date	Account Titles and Explanation	PR	Debit	Credit

2b. **GENERAL JOURNAL** Page____

Date	Account Titles and Explanation	PR	Debit	Credit

Problem 6-13A

Part 1

Inventory Items	Units on Hand	Per Unit		Total Cost	Total NRV	LCNRV applied to:	
		Cost	NRV			a. Major Group	b. Separately to Each Product
Car audio equipment							
Speakers	345	$ 90	$ 98				
Stereos	260	111	100				
Amplifiers	326	86	95				
Subwoofers	204	52	41				
Subtotal							
Security equipment							
Alarms	480	150	125				
Locks	291	93	84				
Cameras	212	310	322				
Subtotal							
Binocular equipment							
Tripods	185	70	84				
Stabilizers	170	97	105				
Subtotal							
Totals							

2   **GENERAL JOURNAL**   Page____

Date	Account Titles and Explanation	PR	Debit	Credit

Problem 6-14A

_____
_____
_____
_____
_____
_____
_____
_____
_____
_____
_____
_____
_____
_____
_____
_____
_____
_____
_____
_____
_____
_____
_____
_____

Name: _____

Problem 6-15A

_____

_____

_____

_____

_____

_____

_____

_____

_____

_____

_____

_____

_____

_____

_____

_____

_____

_____

_____

_____

_____

Fundamental Accounting Principles, 17ce, Working Papers

Name: _____

Problem 6-16A

Part 1

<table>
<tr><td colspan="3" align="center">**Earthly Goods**</td></tr>
<tr><td colspan="3" align="center">**Estimated Inventory**</td></tr>
<tr><td colspan="3" align="center">**December 31, 2023**</td></tr>
<tr><td></td><td>*At Cost*</td><td>*At Retail*</td></tr>
</table>

Part 2

<table>
<tr><td colspan="3" align="center">**Earthly Goods**</td></tr>
<tr><td colspan="3" align="center">**Inventory Shortage**</td></tr>
<tr><td colspan="3" align="center">**December 31, 2023**</td></tr>
<tr><td></td><td>*At Cost*</td><td>*At Retail*</td></tr>
</table>

Name: _____

Problem 6-17A

Part 1

	At Cost	At Retail

Part 2

_____
_____
_____
_____

Problem 6-18A

	2020	2019
a. Inventory turnover ratio		
b. Days' sales in inventory		

Comments:

_____
_____
_____
_____
_____
_____
_____
_____

Name: _____

*Problem 6-19A

Part 1

_____
_____
_____
_____
_____
_____
_____
_____
_____
_____
_____
_____
_____
_____
_____
_____
_____
_____

Part 2

a. FIFO PERIODIC basis:

_____
_____
_____
_____
_____
_____
_____
_____

b. Weighted Average PERIODIC basis:

_____
_____
_____
_____
_____
_____
_____

Name: _____

*Problem 6-1B

Part 1

	Include / Exclude?	Explanation and if applicable, inventory cost.
a.		
b.		
c.		
d.		
e.		

Part 2

Merchandise Inventory	
Unadjusted Balance.	
Adjusted Bal.	

*Problem 6-2B

1a. FIFO Perpetual

Date	Purchases	Sales (at cost)	Inventory Balance

1b. Moving Weighted Average Perpetual

Date	Purchases	Sales (at cost)	Inventory Balance

Name: _____

*Problem 6-2B (cont'd.)

2. **Specific Identification**

Date	Purchases	Sales (at cost)	Inventory Balance

Name: _____

*Problem 6-2B (cont'd.)

3. _____ GENERAL JOURNAL _____ Page____

Date		Account Titles and Explanation	PR	Debit	Credit
a.					
b.					
c.					

Name: _____

*Problem 6-3B

a. FIFO PERIODIC basis:

_____
_____
_____
_____
_____
_____
_____

b. Weighted Average PERIODIC basis:

_____
_____
_____
_____
_____
_____

Problem 6-4B

1a. FIFO Perpetual

Date	Purchases	Sales (at cost)	Inventory Balance

1b. Moving Weighted Average Perpetual

Date	Purchases	Sales (at cost)	Inventory Balance

Name: _____

Problem 6-4B (concl'd.)

2.

	FIFO	Moving Weighted Average
Sales		
Cost of goods sold....................		
Gross profit...........................		

Analysis component: _____
_____
_____
_____
_____
_____

*Problem 6-5B

a. FIFO PERIODIC basis:

_____
_____
_____
_____
_____
_____
_____

b. Weighted Average PERIODIC basis:

_____
_____
_____
_____
_____
_____
_____
_____
_____

Problem 6-6B

1a. FIFO Perpetual

Date	Purchases	Sales (at cost)	Inventory Balance

Name: _____

Problem 6-6B (cont'd.)

1b. Moving Weighted Average Perpetual

Date	Purchases	Sales (at cost)	Inventory Balance

Part 2

	FIFO	Weighted moving average
Sales		
Cost of goods sold		
Gross Profit		

Part 3

Part 4

Fundamental Accounting Principles, 17ce, Working Papers

Name: _____

Problem 6-7B

1a. FIFO Perpetual

te	Purchases			Sales (at cost)			Inventory Balance		
	Units	Unit Cost	Total Cost	Units	Unit Cost	Cost of Goods Sold	Units	Unit Cost	*Total Cost*
1	Beginning inventory 290 @ $82.00 =								
10	205 @ $86.00 =								
20									
30	281 @ $80.00 =								
5	255 @ $66.00 =								
15									
al									

Cost of goods available for sale = *Cost of goods sold* + *Ending inventory*

Problem 6-7B (cont'd)

1b. Moving Weighted Average Perpetual

Date	Purchases			Sales (at cost)			Inventory Balance		
	Units	Unit Cost	Total Cost	Units	Unit Cost	Cost of Goods Sold	Units	Unit Cost	To C
Jan. 1	Beginning inventory 290 @ $82.00 =								
Mar. 10	205 @ $86.00 =								
20									
Apr. 30	281 @ $80.00 =								
July 5	255 @ $66.00 =								
Sep. 15									
Total									

Part 2

	FIFO	Weighted moving average
Sales		
Cost of goods sold		
Gross Profit		

Analysis component:

_____
_____
_____
_____
_____
_____

Fundamental Accounting Principles, 17ce, Working Papers

Problem 6-8B

Blizzard Company
Income Statement Comparing FIFO and Moving Weighted Average Cost
For Year Ended December 31, 2023

	FIFO	Moving Weighted Average
Sales		
Cost of goods sold		
Gross profit		
Operating expenses		
Profit		

Supporting calculations:

_____
_____
_____
_____
_____
_____
_____
_____
_____
_____
_____
_____
_____
_____

Name: _____

Problem 6-8B (cont'd.)

a. FIFO Perpetual

Date	Purchases	Sales (at cost)	Inventory Balance

b. Moving Weighted-Average Perpetual

Date	Purchases	Sales (at cost)	Inventory Balance

Fundamental Accounting Principles, 17ce, Working Papers

Problem 6-8B (concl'd.)

Analysis component:

_____
_____
_____
_____
_____
_____
_____
_____
_____

*Problem 6-9B

Blizzard Company
Income Statement Comparing FIFO and Weighted Average Periodic
For Year Ended December 31, 2023

	FIFO	Weighted Average
Sales		
Cost of goods sold		
Gross profit		
Operating expenses		
Profit		

Supporting calculations:

_____
_____
_____
_____
_____
_____
_____
_____
_____
_____
_____
_____

a. FIFO Periodic

_____
_____
_____
_____
_____
_____
_____
_____
_____
_____

b. Weighted Average Periodic

_____
_____
_____
_____
_____
_____
_____
_____
_____
_____

Problem 6-10B

Part 1

a. Cost of Goods Sold:	2023	2024	2025
Reported.......................................	_____	_____	_____
Adjustments: 12/31/2023 error	_____	_____	_____
12/31/2024 error	_____	_____	_____
Corrected......................................	_____	_____	_____
	_____	_____	_____

b. Profit:	2023	2024	2025
Reported.......................................	_____	_____	_____
Adjustments: 12/31/2023 error	_____	_____	_____
12/31/2024 error	_____	_____	_____
Corrected......................................	_____	_____	_____
	_____	_____	_____

c. Total Current Assets:	2023	2024	2025
Reported.......................................	_____	_____	_____
Adjustments: 12/31/2023 error	_____	_____	_____
12/31/2024 error	_____	_____	_____
Corrected......................................	_____	_____	_____
	_____	_____	_____

d. Equity:	2023	2024	2025
Reported.......................................	_____	_____	_____
Adjustments: 12/31/2023 error	_____	_____	_____
12/31/2024 error	_____	_____	_____
Corrected......................................	_____	_____	_____
	_____	_____	_____

Analysis component:

_____
_____
_____
_____
_____
_____
_____
_____
_____
_____
_____
_____
_____
_____
_____

Problem 6-11B

Part 1

	Incorrect Income Statement Information For Years Ended December 31				Corrected Income Statement Information For Years Ended December 31			
	2023	%	2024	%	2023	%	2024	%
Sales.............................								
Cost of goods sold........								
Gross profit..................								

Part 2 _____

_____
_____
_____

Fundamental Accounting Principles, 17ce, Working Papers

Problem 6-12B

Part 1

Inventory Items	Units on Hand	Per Unit Cost	Per Unit NRV	Total Cost	Total NRV	LCNRV applied to: a. Major Category	LCNRV applied to: b. Separately to Each Product
Office furniture:							
Desks	430	$261	$305				
Credenzas	290	227	256				
Chairs	585	49	43				
Bookshelves	320	93	82				
Filing cabinets:							
Two-drawer	215	81	70				
Four-drawer	400	135	122				
Lateral	178	104	118				
Office Equip.:							
Fax machines	415	168	200				
Copiers	544	317	288				
Typewriters	355	125	117				

2a.   **GENERAL JOURNAL**   Page____

Date	Account Titles and Explanation	PR	Debit	Credit

2b.   **GENERAL JOURNAL**   Page____

Date	Account Titles and Explanation	PR	Debit	Credit

Problem 6-13B

Part 1

Inventory Items	Units on Hand	Per Unit		Total Cost	Total NRV	LCNRV applied to:	
		Cost	NRV			a. Major Category	b. Separately to Each Product
Office furniture:							
Desks	536	$261	$305				
Chairs	395	227	256				
Mats	687	49	43				
Bookshelves	421	93	82				
Filing cabinets:							
Two-drawer	114	81	70				
Four-drawer	298	135	122				
Lateral	75	104	118				
Office Equip.:							
Projectors	370	168	200				
Copiers	475	317	288				
Phones	302	125	117				

Part 2 **GENERAL JOURNAL** Page____

Date		Account Titles and Explanation	PR	Debit	Credit

Problem 6-14B

Name: _____

Problem 6-15B

_____
_____
_____
_____
_____
_____
_____
_____
_____
_____
_____
_____
_____
_____
_____
_____
_____
_____
_____
_____

Name: _____

Problem 6-16B

Part 1

	THE WILKE CO.	
	Estimated Inventory	
	December 31, 2023	
	At Cost	*At Retail*

Part 2

	THE WILKE CO.	
	Inventory Shortage	
	December 31, 2023	
	At Cost	*At Retail*

Problem 6-17B

Part 1

	At Cost	At Retail

Problem 6-18B

	2020	2019
c. Inventory turnover ratio		
d. Days' sales in inventory		

Comments: _____

Name: _____

*Problem 6-19B

Part 1

_____
_____
_____
_____
_____
_____
_____
_____
_____
_____

Part 2

a. FIFO PERIODIC basis:

_____
_____
_____
_____
_____
_____

b. Weighted Average PERIODIC basis:

_____
_____
_____
_____
_____
_____

Name: _____

Quick Study 7-1

(a) _____

_____

_____

_____

_____

_____

_____

(b) _____

_____

_____

_____

_____

_____

_____

(c) _____

_____

_____

_____

Quick Study 7-2

_____

_____

Partial Balance Sheet

_____

_____

_____

_____

_____

_____

Quick Study 7-3

Weakness #1	
Implication	
Recommendation	

Weakness #2	
Implication	
Recommendation	

Weakness #3	
Implication	
Recommendation	

Name: _____

Quick Study 7-4

1. _____

_____

2. _____

_____

3. _____

_____

4. _____

_____

_____

_____

Quick Study 7-5

1. _____
2. _____
3. _____
4. _____
5. _____

Quick Study 7-6

1. _____

_____

2. _____

_____

3. _____

_____

_____

_____

Quick Study 7-7

1. _____

_____

2. _____

_____

3. _____

_____

_____

Chapter 7

Name: _____

Quick Study 7-8

1. _____
2. _____
3. _____
4. _____

Quick Study 7-9

GENERAL JOURNAL

Page____

Date	Account Titles and Explanation	PR	Debit	Credit
1.				
2.				

Copyright © 2022 by McGraw Hill Ltd.

Fundamental Accounting Principles, 17ce, Working Papers

637

Chapter 7

Name: _____

Quick Study 7-10

1. Establishment of the fund:

                        GENERAL JOURNAL   Page____

Date	Account Titles and Explanation	PR	Debit	Credit

2. Summary of petty cash receipts and entry to reimburse the fund at month-end:

Wee Ones Agency
                    Petty Cash Payments Report
                         May 1 – 31, 2023

Fund total
Less: Cash remaining
Equals: Cash required to replenish petty cash
Cash over/(short)

                        GENERAL JOURNAL   Page____

Date	Account Titles and Explanation	PR	Debit	Credit

3. _____

Copyright © 2022 by McGraw Hill Ltd.
Fundamental Accounting Principles, 17ce, Working Papers

Quick Study 7-11

GENERAL JOURNAL   Page____

Date		Account Titles and Explanation	PR	Debit	Credit

Quick Study 7-12

GENERAL JOURNAL   Page____

Date		Account Titles and Explanation	PR	Debit	Credit

Quick Study 7-13

_____
_____
_____
_____
_____
_____

Quick Study 7-14

GENERAL JOURNAL   Page____

Date		Account Titles and Explanation	PR	Debit	Credit

Quick Study 7-15

		GENERAL JOURNAL			Page____
Date		**Account Titles and Explanation**	**PR**	**Debit**	**Credit**

Quick Study 7-16   Parts 1 and 2:

	Bank or Book Side	Add or Subtract	Entry or not
a) Deposits in transit			
b) Interest on average monthly balance			
c) Credit memos			
d) Bank service charges			
e) Outstanding cheques			
f) Debit memos			
g) NSF cheques			

Quick Study 7-17

	Bank or Book Side	Add or Subtract	Entry or not
a) Interest on cash balance			
b) Bank service charges			
c) Minimum balance bank fee			
d) Outstanding cheques			
e) Collection of note by bank			
f) NSF cheques			
g) Deposits in transit			

Quick Study 7-18

Bank Reconciliation			

Quick Study 7-19

Bank Reconciliation			

GENERAL JOURNAL   Page____

Date		Account Titles and Explanation	PR	Debit	Credit

Quick Study 7-20

a. _____

Bank Reconciliation			

b.   GENERAL JOURNAL   Page____

Date		Account Titles and Explanation	PR	Debit	Credit

Quick Study 7-21

Bank Reconciliation

Quick Study 7-22

                                        GENERAL JOURNAL   Page____

Date		Account Titles and Explanation	PR	Debit	Credit

Quick Study 7-23

_____
_____

*Quick Study 7-24

Company A's Quick Ratio	**Company B's Quick Ratio**

Exercise 7-1

_____
_____
_____
_____
_____
_____
_____
_____
_____
_____

Exercise 7-2

_____
_____
_____
_____
_____
_____
_____
_____
_____
_____
_____
_____
_____
_____
_____
_____
_____
_____
_____
_____
_____
_____
_____
_____
_____
_____
_____

Exercise 7-3

	Weakness or Strength	Internal Control Principle
1.		
2.		
3.		
4.		
5.		

Exercise 7-4

(a)

_____

_____

_____

_____

_____

_____

(b)

_____

_____

_____

_____

_____

_____

_____

Exercise 7-5

Internal Control Problem: _____

_____
_____
_____
_____
_____
_____
_____
_____

Internal Control Recommendation: _____

_____
_____
_____
_____
_____

Exercise 7-6

_____
_____
_____
_____
_____
_____
_____
_____
_____
_____

Exercise 7-7

(a) Establish the Fund

GENERAL JOURNAL   Page____

Date		Account Titles and Explanation	PR	Debit	Credit

(b) Prepare a summary of petty cash receipts

Cameron Co.
Petty Cash Payments Report
January 1 – 8, 2023

Receipts:
_____
_____
_____
_____
_____
_____

Fund total
Less: Cash remaining
Equals: Cash required to replenish petty cash
Cash over/(short)

Name: _____

Exercise 7-7 (concl'd.)

Record the reimbursement:

GENERAL JOURNAL

Page____

Date		Account Titles and Explanation	PR	Debit	Credit

Analysis component: _____

_____

_____

_____

_____

_____

Exercise 7-8

(a) Establish the Fund

GENERAL JOURNAL

Page____

Date		Account Titles and Explanation	PR	Debit	Credit

Exercise 7-8 (concl'd.)

(b) Prepare a summary of petty cash receipts

Willard Company
Petty Cash Payments Report
September 9 – 30, 2023

Receipts:

_____

_____

_____

_____

_____

_____

Fund total

Less: Cash remaining

Equals: Cash required to replenish petty cash

Cash over/(short)

Reimburse and reduce the fund

GENERAL JOURNAL   Page____

Date		Account Titles and Explanation	PR	Debit	Credit

Analysis component:

_____

_____

_____

_____

_____

_____

_____

Exercise 7-9

GENERAL JOURNAL Page____

Date	Account Titles and Explanation	PR	Debit	Credit
a.				
b.				
c.				

Exercise 7-10

1. Establish the Fund

GENERAL JOURNAL Page____

Date	Account Titles and Explanation	PR	Debit	Credit

Exercise 7-10 (concl'd.)

2. Prepare a summary of petty cash receipts

Dallas Repairs
Petty Cash Payments Report
July 5– 31, 2023

Receipts:

Fund total

Less: Cash remaining

Equals: Cash required to replenish petty cash

Cash over/(short)

3. Reimburse and reduce the fund

GENERAL JOURNAL   Page_____

Date		Account Titles and Explanation	PR	Debit	Credit

Name: _____

Exercise 7-11

GENERAL JOURNAL   Page____

Date	Account Titles and Explanation	PR	Debit	Credit

GENERAL JOURNAL   Page____

Date		Account Titles and Explanation	PR	Debit	Credit

Exercise 7-12 (concl'd.)

GENERAL JOURNAL

Date	Account Titles and Explanation	PR	Debit	Credit

Analysis component:

_____
_____
_____
_____
_____
_____
_____
_____
_____
_____
_____
_____
_____
_____
_____
_____
_____
_____
_____
_____

Exercise 7-13

		Bank Balance	Book Balance		Shown or Not Shown on Reconciliation
		Add or Subtract	Add or Subtract	Adjust	
1.	NSF check shown on bank statement but not yet recorded by company.				
2.	Interest earned on the account.				
3.	Deposit made on September 5 and processed by bank on September 6.				
4.	Check written by another depositor but charged against this company's account.				
5.	Bank service charge.				
6.	Checks outstanding on August 31 that cleared the bank in September.				
7.	Check written against the company account and cleared by the bank; erroneously not recorded by the company recordkeeper.				
8.	A note receivable is collected by the bank for the company but not yet recorded by the company.				
9.	Checks written and mailed to payees on October 2.				
10.	Checks written by the company and mailed to payees on September 30.				
11.	Deposit made on September 30 after the bank closed.				
12.	Bank fees for check printing are not yet recorded by the company.				

Exercise 7-14

_____
_____

Exercise 7-15

GENERAL JOURNAL   Page____

Date	Account Titles and Explanation	PR	Debit	Credit

Exercise 7-16

_____
_____

Exercise 7-17

Part 1

_____
_____

Part 2

GENERAL JOURNAL

Page____

Date	Account Titles and Explanation	PR	Debit	Credit

Analysis component: _____
_____
_____
_____
_____
_____
_____

Exercise 7-18

a. _____

_____

b.   GENERAL JOURNAL   Page____

Date		Account Titles and Explanation	PR	Debit	Credit

Analysis component:

_____
_____
_____
_____
_____
_____
_____

Exercise 7-19

	Bank Balance		Book Balance			Not Shown on the Reconciliation
	Add	Deduct	Add	Deduct	Adjust	
1. Interest income earned on the account.						
2. Deposit made on September 30 after the bank was closed.						
3. Cheques outstanding on August 31 that cleared the bank in September.						
4. NSF cheque from customer returned on September 15 but not recorded by the company.						
5. Cheques written and mailed to payees on September 30.						
6. Deposit made on September 5 that was processed on Sept. 8.						
7. Bank service charge.						
8. Cheques written and mailed to payees on October 5.						
9. Cheque written by another company but charged against the company's account in error.						
10. Customer payment through electronic funds transfer received in the bank but not recorded in the company's books.						
11. Bank charge for collection of electronic fund transfer in Item 10.						
12. Cheque written against the account and cleared by the bank; not recorded by the bookkeeper.						

Fundamental Accounting Principles, 17ce, Working Papers   661

Chapter 7

Name: _____

Exercise 7-20

	Case X	Case Y	Case Z

Problem 7-1A

(1) Principle Violated:	
Recommendation:	

(2) Principle Violated:	
Recommendation:	

(3) Principle Violated:	
Recommendation:	

(4) Principle Violated:	
Recommendation:	

(5) Principle Violated:	
Recommendation:	

Problem 7-2A

Part 1   **GENERAL JOURNAL**   Page____

Date		Account Titles and Explanation	PR	Debit	Credit

Part 2

Halifax Fitness Consulting
Petty Cash Payments Report
February 2 – 28, 2023

Receipts:

Fund total

Less: Cash remaining

Equals: Cash required to replenish petty cash

Cash over/(short)

Part 3   **GENERAL JOURNAL**   Page____

Date		Account Titles and Explanation	PR	Debit	Credit

Problem 7-2A (concl'd.)

Analysis component: _____

_____
_____
_____
_____
_____
_____
_____
_____

Problem 7-3A

GENERAL JOURNAL   Page____

Date	Account Titles and Explanation	PR	Debit	Credit

Analysis component: _____

_____
_____
_____
_____
_____
_____

Name: _____

Problem 7-4A

GENERAL JOURNAL   Page____

Date	Account Titles and Explanation	PR	Debit	Credit

Analysis component: _____

_____

_____

_____

_____

_____

Problem 7-5A

a.

_____

b.   **GENERAL JOURNAL**   Page____

Date	Account Titles and Explanation	PR	Debit	Credit

Analysis component: _____

_____

_____

_____

_____

_____

_____

Problem 7-6A

a.

_____

_____

_____

b.

GENERAL JOURNAL Page____

Date	Account Titles and Explanation	PR	Debit	Credit

Fundamental Accounting Principles, 17ce, Working Papers

Problem 7-6A (concl'd.)

GENERAL JOURNAL   Page____

Date		Account Titles and Explanation	PR	Debit	Credit

Problem 7-7A

Part 1

_____

_____

Name: _____

Problem 7-7A (concl'd.)

Part 2

GENERAL JOURNAL

Date		Account Titles and Explanation	PR	Debit	Credit

Analysis component: _____

_____

_____

_____

_____

_____

_____

_____

_____

_____

_____

_____

Problem 7-8A

Part 1

_____

Part 2

GENERAL JOURNAL

Page____

Date	Account Titles and Explanation	PR	Debit	Credit

Problem 7-8A (concl'd.)

Analysis component: _____

_____

_____

_____

_____

_____

_____

_____

_____

_____

_____

Problem 7-9A

a. _____

_____

b.

GENERAL JOURNAL

Page____

Date	Account Titles and Explanation	PR	Debit	Credit

Problem 7-10A

a. _____

_____

b.   **GENERAL JOURNAL**   Page____

Date	Account Titles and Explanation	PR	Debit	Credit

Problem 7-11A

Part 1

Part 2

GENERAL JOURNAL   Page____

Date		Account Titles and Explanation	PR	Debit	Credit

Problem 7-11A (concl'd.)

GENERAL JOURNAL

Page____

Date		Account Titles and Explanation	PR	Debit	Credit

Analysis component:

_____

_____

_____

_____

_____

_____

_____

Problem 7-1B

(1) **Principle Violated:**
Recommendation:

(2) **Principle Violated:**
Recommendation:

(3) **Principle Violated:**
Recommendation:

(4) **Principle Violated:**
Recommendation:

(5) **Principle Violated:**
Recommendation:

Problem 7-2B

Part 1   GENERAL JOURNAL   Page____

Date	Account Titles and Explanation	PR	Debit	Credit

Part 2

Baby Photography
Petty Cash Payments Report
July 5 – 31, 2023

Receipts:

Fund total

Less: Cash remaining

Equals: Cash required to replenish petty cash

Cash over/(short)

Part 3   GENERAL JOURNAL   Page____

Date	Account Titles and Explanation	PR	Debit	Credit

Problem 7-2B (concl'd.)

Analysis component: _____

_____

_____

_____

_____

_____

_____

_____

Problem 7-3B

GENERAL JOURNAL   Page____

Date	Account Titles and Explanation	PR	Debit	Credit

Analysis component: _____

_____

_____

_____

_____

_____

Problem 7-4B

GENERAL JOURNAL

Date	Account Titles and Explanation	PR	Debit	Credit

Analysis component: _____

Advantage   Disadvantage

_____
_____
_____
_____
_____

Problem 7-5B

a.

_____
_____
_____

b. <div align="center">**GENERAL JOURNAL**</div> Page____

Date	Account Titles and Explanation	PR	Debit	Credit

Analysis component: _____
_____
_____
_____
_____
_____
_____

Problem 7-6B

a.

_____

_____

_____

b.

GENERAL JOURNAL

Page____

Date	Account Titles and Explanation	PR	Debit	Credit

Problem 7-7B

Part 1

_____
_____
_____

Part 2

GENERAL JOURNAL

Page____

Date	Account Titles and Explanation	PR	Debit	Credit

Name: _____

Problem 7-7B (concl'd.)

Analysis component: _____

_____
_____
_____
_____
_____
_____
_____
_____

Problem 7-8B   Part 1

_____
_____

Part 2   **GENERAL JOURNAL**   Page____

Date	Account Titles and Explanation	PR	Debit	Credit

Problem 7-8B (concl'd.)

GENERAL JOURNAL

Page____

Date	Account Titles and Explanation	PR	Debit	Credit

Analysis component: _____

_____

_____

_____

_____

_____

_____

_____

_____

_____

_____

Problem 7-9B   Part 1

_____

_____

_____

Part 2   GENERAL JOURNAL   Page____

Date	Account Titles and Explanation	PR	Debit	Credit

Problem 7-10B   Part 1

_____

Part 2   GENERAL JOURNAL   Page____

Date	Account Titles and Explanation	PR	Debit	Credit

Name: _____

Problem 7-11B   Part 1

Problem 7-11B (concl'd.)

Part 2

GENERAL JOURNAL

Date	Account Titles and Explanation	PR	Debit	Credit

Analysis component: _____

_____

_____

_____

_____

_____

_____

Name: _____

Quick Study 8-1

GENERAL JOURNAL

Date		Account Titles and Explanation	PR	Debit	Credit

Quick Study 8-2

a. _____
_____
_____
_____
_____

b. _____
_____
_____
_____

c. _____
_____
_____
_____

d. _____
_____
_____
_____

Name: _____

Quick Study 8-3

GENERAL JOURNAL

Date		Account Titles and Explanation	PR	Debit	Credit

Name: _____

Quick Study 8-4

Biotech
Partial Balance Sheet
December 31, 2023

Quick Study 8-5

GENERAL JOURNAL

Date		Account Titles and Explanation	PR	Debit	Credit

Quick Study 8-6

a.

Allowance for Doubtful Accounts

b.

_____

_____

_____

_____

_____

c.

GENERAL JOURNAL   Page____

Date	Account Titles and Explanation	PR	Debit	Credit

Quick Study 8-7

Allowance for Doubtful Accounts

GENERAL JOURNAL   Page____

Date	Account Titles and Explanation	PR	Debit	Credit

Name: _____

Quick Study 8-8

a.

| GENERAL JOURNAL | Page____ |

Date	Account Titles and Explanation	PR	Debit	Credit

b. _____

_____

c. _____

_____

Quick Study 8-9

GENERAL JOURNAL   Page____

Date	Account Titles and Explanation	PR	Debit	Credit

Allowance for Doubtful Accounts

Quick Study 8-10

GENERAL JOURNAL   Page____

Date	Account Titles and Explanation	PR	Debit	Credit

Name: _____

Quick Study 8-11

GENERAL JOURNAL
Page____

Date		Account Titles and Explanation	PR	Debit	Credit

Quick Study 8-12

GENERAL JOURNAL

Date		Account Titles and Explanation	PR	Debit	Credit

Quick Study 8-13

GENERAL JOURNAL

Date		Account Titles and Explanation	PR	Debit	Credit

Quick Study 8-14

1. Maturity date is _____, which is computed as follows:

    Days in March...
    Minus the date of the note...
    Days remaining in March..
    Add days in April to equal 60 days ....
    Period of the note in days...

    Interest Expense is $_____. Computed as _____

2. Maturity date is _____, which is computed as follows:

    Days in May...
    Minus the date of the note...
    Days remaining in May...
    Add days in June ....
    Add days in July..
    Add days in August to equal 90 days..
    Period of the note in days...

    Interest Expense is $_____. Computed as _____

3. Maturity date is _____, which is computed as follows:

    Days in October...
    Minus the date of the note...
    Days remaining in October ....
    Add days in November..
    Add days in December to equal 45 days ....
    Period of the note in days...

    Interest Expense is $_____. Computed as _____

Quick Study 8-15

1. Maturity date is _____, which is computed as follows:

   Days in August..
   Minus the date of the note..
   Days remaining in August..
   Add days in September...
   Add days in October to equal 90 days ....
   Period of the note in days..

   Interest Expense is $_____. Computed as _____

2.   **GENERAL JOURNAL**

Date		Account Titles and Explanation	PR	Debit	Credit

Quick Study 8-16

GENERAL JOURNAL

Date		Account Titles and Explanation	PR	Debit	Credit

Quick Study 8-17

1.   GENERAL JOURNAL

Date		Account Titles and Explanation	PR	Debit	Credit

2.   Maturity Date   GENERAL JOURNAL

Date		Account Titles and Explanation	PR	Debit	Credit

Quick Study 8-18

_____
_____
_____
_____
_____
_____
_____

Quick Study 8-19

a. _____
b. _____
c. _____

*****Quick Study 8-20**

Year 1: _____

Year 2: _____

*Quick Study 8-21

GENERAL JOURNAL

Date		Account Titles and Explanation	PR	Debit	Credit

*Quick Study 8-22

GENERAL JOURNAL

Date		Account Titles and Explanation	PR	Debit	Credit

*Quick Study 8-23

GENERAL JOURNAL

Date		Account Titles and Explanation	PR	Debit	Credit

Calculations:

_____
_____
_____
_____
_____
_____
_____

Name: _____

Exercise 8-1

Part 1

GENERAL LEDGER

Accounts Receivable	Sales	Sales Returns and Allowances

ACCOUNTS RECEIVABLE SUBLEDGER

ABC Shop	Colt Enterprises	Red McKenzie

Part 2

Comparison:

Fundamental Accounting Principles, 17ce, Working Papers

Chapter 8

Name: _____

Exercise 8-2

1. _____
_____
_____
_____
_____

2. _____
_____
_____
_____
_____

3. _____
_____
_____
_____

4. _____
_____
_____
_____
_____

Exercise 8-3

1.

Weakness #1	
Implication	
Recommendation	
Weakness #2	
Implication	
Recommendation	

Exercise 8-3 (cont'd.)

Weakness #3	
Implication	
Recommendation	
Weakness #4	
Implication	
Recommendation	

2. _____

_____

_____

_____

_____

_____

_____

_____

_____

_____

Name: _____

Exercise 8-4

GENERAL JOURNAL

Date		Account Titles and Explanation	PR	Debit	Credit

Exercise 8-5

GENERAL JOURNAL

Date		Account Titles and Explanation	PR	Debit	Credit

Exercise 8-6

GENERAL JOURNAL

Date		Account Titles and Explanation	PR	Debit	Credit

Exercise 8-7

a.

Accounts Receivable		Allowance for Doubtful Accounts

GENERAL JOURNAL

Date	Account Titles and Explanation	PR	Debit	Credit

b.

Accounts Receivable		Allowance for Doubtful Accounts

GENERAL JOURNAL

Date	Account Titles and Explanation	PR	Debit	Credit

Fundamental Accounting Principles, 17ce, Working Papers

Exercise 8-8

1.

GENERAL JOURNAL

Date		Account Titles and Explanation	PR	Debit	Credit

2.

Accounts Receivable

Allowance for Doubtful Accounts

Bad Debt Expense

Exercise 8-9

a. _____

b. _____

c. _____

d. _____

e. _____

Exercise 8-10

Partial Balance Sheet		

Exercise 8-11

a, b, and c   **GENERAL JOURNAL**   Page____

Date		Account Titles and Explanation	PR	Debit	Credit

Calculations:

Accounts Receivable   **Allowance for Doubtful Accounts**

Name: _____

Exercise 8-11 (concl'd.)

d.

Partial Balance Sheet		

Analysis component:

_____
_____
_____
_____
_____
_____

Exercise 8-12

a, b, and c.   GENERAL JOURNAL   Page____

Date	Account Titles and Explanation	PR	Debit	Credit

Exercise 8-12 (concl'd.)

Calculations:

Accounts Receivable	Allowance for Doubtful Accounts

d.

Partial Balance Sheet		

Analysis component:

_____
_____
_____
_____
_____
_____

Exercise 8-13

a and b.

GENERAL JOURNAL   Page____

Date		Account Titles and Explanation	PR	Debit	Credit

Calculations:

Accounts Receivable	Allowance for Doubtful Accounts

c.

Partial Balance Sheet

Analysis component:

_____

_____

_____

_____

_____

_____

Name: _____

Exercise 8-14

GENERAL JOURNAL

Page____

Date		Account Titles and Explanation	PR	Debit	Credit

Analysis component:

_____
_____
_____
_____
_____
_____
_____
_____
_____

Exercise 8-15

1. _____
_____
_____
_____

2. _____
_____
_____

3. _____

GENERAL JOURNAL

Page____

Date		Account Titles and Explanation	PR	Debit	Credit

Name: _____

Exercise 8-16

GENERAL JOURNAL

Date		Account Titles and Explanation	PR	Debit	Credit

Exercise 8-17

GENERAL JOURNAL

Date		Account Titles and Explanation	PR	Debit	Credit

Name: _____

Exercise 8-18

GENERAL JOURNAL

Date		Account Titles and Explanation	PR	Debit	Credit

Exercise 8-19

Part 1

Accounts Receivable Turnover	Days Sales Outstanding

Part 2

_____
_____
_____
_____
_____
_____
_____

Exercise 8-20

GENERAL JOURNAL

Date		Account Titles and Explanation	PR	Debit	Credit

Name: _____

Exercise 8-21

GENERAL JOURNAL

Date		Account Titles and Explanation	PR	Debit	Credit

Exercise 8-22

GENERAL JOURNAL

Date		Account Titles and Explanation	PR	Debit	Credit

Exercise 8-23

GENERAL JOURNAL

Date		Account Titles and Explanation	PR	Debit	Credit

*Exercise 8-24

GENERAL JOURNAL

Date	Account Titles and Explanation	PR	Debit	Credit

Financial Statement Note(s):

_____
_____
_____
_____

*Exercise 8-25

GENERAL JOURNAL

Date		Account Titles and Explanation	PR	Debit	Credit

Calculations:

_____
_____
_____
_____
_____
_____

Problem 8-1A

Performance _____
_____
_____

Measurability _____
_____
_____

Collectability _____
_____
_____
_____

Conclusion _____
_____
_____

Problem 8-2A
Part 1

a. Expense is 2% of credit sales:

GENERAL JOURNAL

Date	Account Titles and Explanation	PR	Debit	Credit

b. Allowance is 5% of accounts receivable:

GENERAL JOURNAL

Date	Account Titles and Explanation	PR	Debit	Credit

Calculations for Part b:

Allowance for
Doubtful Accounts

Problem 8-2A (cont'd.)

Part 2

Part 3

Analysis component:

_____

_____

_____

_____

_____

Problem 8-3A   Part 1

Calculation of the required balance of the allowance (using an aging analysis):

Not due:	
1 to 30:	
31 to 60:	
61 to 90:	
Over 90:	

Allowance for Doubtful Accounts

Part 2

GENERAL JOURNAL

Date	Account Titles and Explanation	PR	Debit	Credit

Analysis component:

_____

_____

_____

_____

_____

Chapter 8

Name: _____

Problem 8-4A   Part 1

Calculation of the required balance of the allowance (using an aging analysis):

Not due:	
1 to 30:	
31 to 60:	
61 to 90:	
Over 90:	

Allowance for Doubtful Accounts

Part 2

GENERAL JOURNAL

Date	Account Titles and Explanation	PR	Debit	Credit

Analysis component:

Problem 8-5A   Part A

GENERAL JOURNAL Page____

Date		Account Titles and Explanation	PR	Debit	Credit

Fundamental Accounting Principles, 17ce, Working Papers

Name: _____

Problem 8-5A (concl'd.)

Part B

Part 2   GENERAL JOURNAL   Page____

Date		Account Titles and Explanation	PR	Debit	Credit

Part 3

	Account Titles and Explanation			Debit	Credit

Part 4

_____

_____

Part C

Part 5   GENERAL JOURNAL   Page____

Date		Account Titles and Explanation	PR	Debit	Credit

Calculations:

Accounts Receivable	Allowance for Doubtful Accounts

Part 6

			Debit	Credit

Part 7

_____

_____

Problem 8-6A

GENERAL JOURNAL

Date	Account Titles and Explanation	PR	Debit	Credit
2023				
a.				
b.				
c.				
d.				

Calculations:

Accounts Receivable	Allowance for Doubtful Accounts

Problem 8-6A (concl'd.)

GENERAL JOURNAL

Date	Account Titles and Explanation	PR	Debit	Credit
2024				
e.				
f.				
g.				
h.				

Calculations:

Accounts Receivable   **Allowance for Doubtful Accounts**

Name: _____

Problem 8-7A

Part 1

a.

GENERAL JOURNAL

Date	Account Titles and Explanation	PR	Debit	Credit
2023				

Allowance for Doubtful Accounts

b.

Part2

c.

GENERAL JOURNAL

Date	Account Titles and Explanation	PR	Debit	Credit
2023				

Calculations:

Allowance for Doubtful Accounts

d.

Problem 8-8A

Part 1

GENERAL JOURNAL

Date		Account Titles and Explanation	PR	Debit	Credit

Part 2

GENERAL JOURNAL

Date		Account Titles and Explanation	PR	Debit	Credit

Calculations:

Accounts Receivable	Allowance for Doubtful Accounts

Name: _____

Problem 8-9A

a.

<table>
<tr><th rowspan="2">Customer</th><th colspan="6">Month</th></tr>
<tr><th>Not yet
due
0.5%</th><th>1 to 29
days past
due
1%</th><th>30 to 59
days past
due
4%</th><th>60 to 89
days past
due
10%</th><th>90 to 119
days past
due
20%</th><th>Over 119
days past
due
50%</th></tr>
<tr><td>B. Axley</td><td></td><td></td><td></td><td></td><td></td><td></td></tr>
<tr><td>T. Holton</td><td></td><td></td><td></td><td></td><td></td><td></td></tr>
<tr><td>W. Nix</td><td></td><td></td><td></td><td></td><td></td><td></td></tr>
<tr><td>C. Percy</td><td></td><td></td><td></td><td></td><td></td><td></td></tr>
<tr><td>K. Willis</td><td></td><td></td><td></td><td></td><td></td><td></td></tr>
<tr><td></td><td></td><td></td><td></td><td></td><td></td><td></td></tr>
<tr><td></td><td></td><td></td><td></td><td></td><td></td><td></td></tr>
<tr><td></td><td></td><td></td><td></td><td></td><td></td><td></td></tr>
<tr><td></td><td></td><td></td><td></td><td></td><td></td><td></td></tr>
</table>

b.   **GENERAL JOURNAL**   Page____

Date	Account Titles and Explanation	PR	Debit	Credit

Calculations:

Accounts Receivable	Allowance for Doubtful Accounts

Problem 8-10A

a.

GENERAL JOURNAL   Page____

Date	Account Titles and Explanation	PR	Debit	Credit
2023				
2024				
2025				

Calculations:

Accounts Receivable   **Allowance for Doubtful Accounts**

Analysis component:

_____

_____

_____

_____

_____

Problem 8-11A

Parts a, b, and c.

Date of Note	Principal	Interest Rate	Term	Maturity Date	Days of Accrued Interest at Dec. 31, 2023	Accrued Interest at Dec. 31, 2023
Nov. 1/22	$240,000	4%	180 days			
Jan. 5/23	$100,000	5%	90 days			
Nov. 20/23	$90,000	4.5%	45 days			
Dec. 10/23	$120,000	5.5%	30 days			

Calculations:

_____
_____
_____
_____
_____
_____
_____
_____
_____
_____
_____
_____
_____
_____
_____
_____

d.   **GENERAL JOURNAL**   Page____

Date	Account Titles and Explanation	PR	Debit	Credit

e.   **GENERAL JOURNAL**   Page____

Date	Account Titles and Explanation	PR	Debit	Credit

Problem 8-12A

Parts a, b, and c.

Date of Note	Principal	Interest Rate	Term	Maturity Date	Days of Accrued Interest at Jul. 31, 2023	Accrued Interest at Jul. 31, 2023
Dec. 1/22	$170,000	4%	180 days			
April 5/23	$71,000	5%	90 days			
June 20/23	$64,000	4.5%	45 days			
July 10/23	$85,000	5.5%	30 days			

Calculations:

_____
_____
_____
_____
_____
_____
_____
_____
_____
_____
_____
_____
_____
_____

d.   **GENERAL JOURNAL**   Page____

Date	Account Titles and Explanation	PR	Debit	Credit

e.   **GENERAL JOURNAL**   Page____

Date	Account Titles and Explanation	PR	Debit	Credit

Problem 8-13A

a.   **GENERAL JOURNAL**   Page____

Date		Account Titles and Explanation	PR	Debit	Credit

Problem 8-13A (concl'd.)

b. Determine the maturity date of the note dated March 2:

_____
_____
_____
_____
_____
_____
_____
_____

Prepare the entry on the maturity date:

GENERAL JOURNAL   Page____

Date	Account Titles and Explanation	PR	Debit	Credit

Name: _____

Problem 8-14A

Parts a. to f.

Page____

Date	Account Titles and Explanation	PR	Debit	Credit

Analysis component:

_____

_____

_____

_____

_____

Name: _____

Problem 8-15A

	2020	2019
a. Accounts receivable turnover ratio		
b. Days sales outstanding		

Comments: _____

_____

_____

_____

_____

_____

_____

Fundamental Accounting Principles, 17ce, Working Papers

739

*Problem 8-16A

GENERAL JOURNAL   Page____

Date	Account Titles and Explanation	PR	Debit	Credit

Analysis component: _____
_____
_____
_____
_____
_____

*Problem 8-17A

GENERAL JOURNAL

Date		Account Titles and Explanation	PR	Debit	Credit

Name: _____

*Problem 8-17A (cont'd.)

GENERAL JOURNAL

Page____

Date	Account Titles and Explanation	PR	Debit	Credit

Name: _____

*Problem 8-18A

GENERAL JOURNAL

Page____

Date		Account Titles and Explanation	PR	Debit	Credit

*Problem 8-18A (cont'd.)

GENERAL JOURNAL

Date	Account Titles and Explanation	PR	Debit	Credit

Analysis component

Financial Statement Note(s):

Explanation: _____

_____

_____

_____

_____

_____

Problem 8-1B

Performance
_____
_____
_____

Measurability
_____
_____
_____

Collectability
_____
_____
_____
_____

Conclusion
_____
_____
_____
_____
_____
_____
_____
_____
_____
_____

Name: _____

Problem 8-2B
Part 1

a. **Expense is 3% of credit sales:**

GENERAL JOURNAL

Date		Account Titles and Explanation	PR	Debit	Credit

b. **Allowance is 6% of accounts receivable:**

GENERAL JOURNAL

Date		Account Titles and Explanation	PR	Debit	Credit

Calculations for Part b:

Allowance for Doubtful Accounts

Part 2

Part 3

Analysis component:

_____
_____
_____
_____
_____

Name: _____

Problem 8-3B   Part 1

Calculation of the required balance of the allowance (using an aging analysis):

Not due:	
1 to 30:	
31 to 60:	
61 to 90:	
Over 90:	

Allowance for Doubtful Accounts

Part 2

GENERAL JOURNAL

Date	Account Titles and Explanation	PR	Debit	Credit

Analysis component:

Problem 8-4B   Part 1

Calculation of the required balance of the allowance (using an aging analysis):

Not due:	
1 to 30:	
31 to 60:	
61 to 90:	
Over 90:	

Allowance for Doubtful Accounts

Part 2

GENERAL JOURNAL

Date	Account Titles and Explanation	PR	Debit	Credit

Analysis component:

Name: _____

Problem 8-5B   Part A

Part 1   **GENERAL JOURNAL**   Page____

Date		Account Titles and Explanation	PR	Debit	Credit

Name: _____

Problem 8-5B (concl'd.)

Part B

Part 2   GENERAL JOURNAL   Page____

Date	Account Titles and Explanation	PR	Debit	Credit

Part 3

Part 4

_____

_____

Part C

Part 5   GENERAL JOURNAL   Page____

Date	Account Titles and Explanation	PR	Debit	Credit

Calculations:

Accounts Receivable	Allowance for Doubtful Accounts

Part 6

Part 7

_____

_____

Problem 8-6B

GENERAL JOURNAL

Date	Account Titles and Explanation	PR	Debit	Credit
2023				
a.				
b.				
c.				
d.				

Calculations:

Accounts Receivable	Allowance for Doubtful Accounts

Name: _____

Problem 8-6B (concl'd.)

GENERAL JOURNAL

Date	Account Titles and Explanation	PR	Debit	Credit
2024				
e.				
f.				
g.				
h.				

Calculations:

Accounts Receivable	Allowance for Doubtful Accounts

Problem 8-7B

Part 1

Part a

GENERAL JOURNAL

Date	Account Titles and Explanation	PR	Debit	Credit
2023				

Allowance for Doubtful Accounts

Part b

Part 2

Part c

GENERAL JOURNAL

Date	Account Titles and Explanation	PR	Debit	Credit
2023				

Calculations:

Allowance for Doubtful Accounts

Part d

Problem 8-8B

Part 1

GENERAL JOURNAL

Date	Account Titles and Explanation	PR	Debit	Credit

Part 2

GENERAL JOURNAL

Date	Account Titles and Explanation	PR	Debit	Credit

Calculations:

Accounts Receivable	Allowance for Doubtful Accounts

Problem 8-9B

a.

<table>
<tr><th rowspan="2">Customer</th><th colspan="6">Month</th></tr>
<tr><th>Not yet due
1.5%</th><th>1 to 29 days past due
2%</th><th>30 to 59 days past due
5%</th><th>60 to 89 days past due
20%</th><th>90 to 119 days past due
35%</th><th>Over 119 days past due
50%</th></tr>
<tr><td>A. Leslie</td><td></td><td></td><td></td><td></td><td></td><td></td></tr>
<tr><td>T. Meston</td><td></td><td></td><td></td><td></td><td></td><td></td></tr>
<tr><td>P. Obrian</td><td></td><td></td><td></td><td></td><td></td><td></td></tr>
<tr><td>L. Timms</td><td></td><td></td><td></td><td></td><td></td><td></td></tr>
<tr><td>W. Victor</td><td></td><td></td><td></td><td></td><td></td><td></td></tr>
<tr><td></td><td></td><td></td><td></td><td></td><td></td><td></td></tr>
<tr><td></td><td></td><td></td><td></td><td></td><td></td><td></td></tr>
<tr><td></td><td></td><td></td><td></td><td></td><td></td><td></td></tr>
<tr><td></td><td></td><td></td><td></td><td></td><td></td><td></td></tr>
</table>

b.   **GENERAL JOURNAL**   Page____

Date		Account Titles and Explanation	PR	Debit	Credit

Calculations:

Accounts Receivable   **Allowance for Doubtful Accounts**

Problem 8-10B

GENERAL JOURNAL

Page_____

Date	Account Titles and Explanation	PR	Debit	Credit
2023				
2024				
2025				

Calculations:

Accounts Receivable		Allowance for Doubtful Accounts	

Analysis component:

_____
_____
_____
_____
_____

Problem 8-11B

Parts a, b, and c.

Date of Note	Principal	Interest Rate	Term	Maturity Date	Days of Accrued Interest at Dec. 31, 2023	Accrued Interest at Dec. 31, 2023
Sept. 20/22	$490,000	3%	120 days			
June 01/23	$240,000	3.5%	45 days			
Nov. 23/23	$164,000	4.5%	90 days			
Dec. 18/23	$120,000	4%	30 days			

Calculations:

_____
_____
_____
_____
_____
_____
_____
_____
_____
_____
_____
_____
_____
_____
_____

d.   **GENERAL JOURNAL**   Page____

Date	Account Titles and Explanation	PR	Debit	Credit

e.   **GENERAL JOURNAL**   Page____

Date	Account Titles and Explanation	PR	Debit	Credit

Problem 8-12B

Parts a, b, and c.

Date of Note	Principal	Interest Rate	Term	Maturity Date	Days of Accrued Interest at Dec. 31, 2023	Accrued Interest at Dec. 31, 2023
Nov. 01/22	$370,000	3%	180 days			
Jan. 05/23	$212,000	3.5%	120 days			
Nov. 20/23	$102,000	4.5%	90 days			
Dec. 10/23	$135,000	5.5%	30 days			

Calculations:

_____
_____
_____
_____
_____
_____
_____
_____
_____
_____
_____
_____
_____
_____
_____

d.   **GENERAL JOURNAL**   Page____

Date	Account Titles and Explanation	PR	Debit	Credit

e.   **GENERAL JOURNAL**   Page____

Date	Account Titles and Explanation	PR	Debit	Credit

Problem 8-13B

a.

GENERAL JOURNAL

Page_____

Date		Account Titles and Explanation	PR	Debit	Credit

Name: _____

Problem 8-13B (concl'd.)

b. Determine the maturity date of the note dated March 1:

_____

_____

_____

_____

_____

_____

Prepare the entry on the maturity date:

GENERAL JOURNAL   Page____

Date	Account Titles and Explanation	PR	Debit	Credit

Name: _____

Problem 8-14B

Parts a. to f.

GENERAL JOURNAL   Page____

Date		Account Titles and Explanation	PR	Debit	Credit

Analysis component: _____

_____

_____

_____

_____

_____

Name: _____

Problem 8-15B

	2020	**2019**
a. Accounts receivable turnover ratio		
b. Days sales in inventory		

Comments: _____
_____
_____
_____
_____
_____
_____
_____

Name: _____

*Problem 8-16B

GENERAL JOURNAL   Page____

Date		Account Titles and Explanation	PR	Debit	Credit

Analysis component: _____
_____
_____
_____
_____

Name: _____

*Problem 8-17B

GENERAL JOURNAL   Page____

Date	Account Titles and Explanation	PR	Debit	Credit

*Problem 8-17B (cont'd.)

GENERAL JOURNAL　　　　　　　　　Page____

Date	Account Titles and Explanation	PR	Debit	Credit

*Problem 8-18B

Part 1

GENERAL JOURNAL

Page____

Date		Account Titles and Explanation	PR	Debit	Credit

*Problem 8-18B (concl'd.)

GENERAL JOURNAL Page____

Date	Account Titles and Explanation	PR	Debit	Credit

Part 2

Financial Statement Note(s):

Explanation: _____
_____
_____
_____
_____
_____

Quick Study 9-1

_____
_____
_____

Quick Study 9-2

_____
_____
_____
_____
_____
_____
_____

Quick Study 9-3

(1)
(a) _____ (c) _____
(b) _____ (d) _____

(2)

GENERAL JOURNAL   Page____

Date	Account Titles and Explanation	PR	Debit	Credit

Quick Study 9-4

PPE Item	(a) Appraised Values	(b) Ratio of Individual Appraised Value to Total Appraised Value (a) ÷ Total Appraised Value	(c) Cost Allocation (b) × Total Actual Cost
Land			
Building			
Totals			

GENERAL JOURNAL   Page____

Date		Account Titles and Explanation	PR	Debit	Credit

Quick Study 9-5

Partial Balance Sheet			

Quick Study 9-6

_____
_____
_____
_____
_____

Quick Study 9-7

1. _____

2. _____

Name:_____

Quick Study 9-8

_____

_____

Year	Calculation	Annual Depreciation
2023		
2024		
2025		
2026		
2027		
Total		

Quick Study 9-9

_____

_____

Year	Calculation	Annual Depreciation
2023		
2024		
2025		
2026		
2027		
Total		

Quick Study 9-10

_____

_____

_____

_____

_____

_____

_____

_____

_____

_____

_____

_____

_____

_____

_____

_____

_____

_____

_____

_____

Quick Study 9-11

a. _____
_____
_____

b. _____
_____
_____
_____

Quick Study 9-12

a. _____
_____
_____

b. _____
_____
_____

Quick Study 9-13

a. _____
_____
_____

b. _____
_____
_____

Quick Study 9-14

_____
_____
_____
_____
_____
_____
_____

Quick Study 9-15

GENERAL JOURNAL Page____

Date		Account Titles and Explanation	PR	Debit	Credit

Calculations:
_____
_____
_____
_____
_____
_____
_____
_____
_____

Quick Study 9-16
_____
_____
_____
_____
_____
_____
_____
_____
_____
_____
_____
_____
_____
_____

Name: _____

Quick Study 9-17

_____
_____
_____
_____
_____

Calculations:

Asset	Cost	Accumulated Depreciation	Book Value	Recoverable Amount	Impairment Loss
Building	$1,200,000	$465,000		$735,000	
Computer	3,500	1,800		200	
Furniture	79,000	53,000		5,000	
Land	630,000	0		790,000	
Machine	284,000	117,000		172,000	

a.

GENERAL JOURNAL

Page____

Date		Account Titles and Explanation	PR	Debit	Credit

b.

GENERAL JOURNAL

Page____

Date		Account Titles and Explanation	PR	Debit	Credit

c.

GENERAL JOURNAL

Page____

Date		Account Titles and Explanation	PR	Debit	Credit

d.

GENERAL JOURNAL

Page____

Date		Account Titles and Explanation	PR	Debit	Credit

Quick Study 9-19

GENERAL JOURNAL   Page____

Date	Account Titles and Explanation	PR	Debit	Credit

Calculations: _____
_____
_____
_____
_____

Quick Study 9-20

GENERAL JOURNAL   Page____

Date	Account Titles and Explanation	PR	Debit	Credit

Calculations: _____
_____

Name:_____

Quick Study 9-21

GENERAL JOURNAL

Page____

Date		Account Titles and Explanation	PR	Debit	Credit

Calculations:
_____
_____
_____

Quick Study 9-22

GENERAL JOURNAL

Page____

Date		Account Titles and Explanation	PR	Debit	Credit

Quick Study 9-23

GENERAL JOURNAL Page____

Date	Account Titles and Explanation	PR	Debit	Credit

Quick Study 9-24

GENERAL JOURNAL Page____

Date	Account Titles and Explanation	PR	Debit	Credit

Calculations: _____
_____
_____
_____

*Quick Study 9-25

	Calculation	
Motor (old)		
Motor (new)		
Metal housing		
Misc. parts		
Total depreciation expense to be recorded on the machine for 2023 =		

Exercise 9-1

Name: _____

Exercise 9-2

Cost of land:

_____
_____
_____
_____
_____
_____
_____
_____

Cost of new building:

_____
_____
_____
_____
_____
_____
_____
_____

Journal entry:

GENERAL JOURNAL

Page____

Date	Account Titles and Explanation	PR	Debit	Credit

Exercise 9-3

PPE Asset	(a) Appraised Values	(b) Ratio of Individual Appraised Value to Total Appraised Value (a) ÷ Total Appraised Value	(c) Cost Allocation (b) × Total Actual Cost
Land			
Land Imp.			
Building			
Totals			

Journal entry:

GENERAL JOURNAL Page____

Date	Account Titles and Explanation	PR	Debit	Credit

Name: _____

Exercise 9-4

GENERAL JOURNAL

Page____

Date		Account Titles and Explanation	PR	Debit	Credit

Calculations:

PPE Asset	(a) Appraised Values	(b) Ratio of Individual Appraised Value to Total Appraised Value (a) ÷ Total Appraised Value	(c) Cost Allocation (b) × Total Actual Cost
Land			
Building			
Equip.			
Tools			
Totals			

Exercise 9-5

GENERAL JOURNAL

Page____

Date	Account Titles and Explanation	PR	Debit	Credit

Calculations: _____

_____

_____

_____

_____

_____

_____

_____

Name: _____

Exercise 9-6

Year	Straight-Line	Double-Declining-Balance	Units-of-Production
2021			
2022			
2023			
2024			
TOTAL			

Calculations:

a. _____

_____

_____

b. _____

_____

_____

_____

_____

_____

_____

c. _____

_____

_____

_____

_____

_____

_____

_____

Fundamental Accounting Principles, 17ce, Working Papers

Chapter 9   Name:_____

Exercise 9-7

a. _____
_____

b. _____
_____

c. _____
_____

Analysis component: _____
_____
_____
_____
_____
_____
_____
_____
_____

Exercise 9-8

Year	Straight-Line Method	
	Depreciation Expense	Book Value at December 31
2023		
2024		
2025		
2026		
2027		

Year	Double-Declining Balance Method	
	Depreciation Expense	Book Value at December 31
2023		
2024		
2025		
2026		
2027		

Year	Units-of-Production Method	
	Depreciation Expense	Book Value at December 31
2023		
2024		
2025		
2026		
2027		

Analysis component:

a. _____

b. _____

Exercise 9-9

Step 1: Cost allocation

PPE Asset	(a) Appraised Values	(b) Ratio of Individual Appraised Value to Total Appraised Value *(a) ÷ Total Appraised Value*	(c) Cost Allocation *(b) × Total Actual Cost*
Land			
Building			
Equip.			
Tools			
Totals			

Step 2: Calculate depreciation

PPE asset	Cost (from c above)	2023 Depreciation	2024 Depreciation
Land			
Building			
Equip.			
Tools			

Analysis component:

_____

_____

_____

_____

_____

_____

_____

Exercise 9-10

Description	Date of Purchase	Cost Information Depreciation Method	Cost	Residual Value	Life	Balance of Accum. Deprec. Dec. 31, 2022	Depreciation Depreciation Expense for 2023	Balance of Accum. Deprec. Dec. 31, 2023
Building	May 2, 2017	S/L	$650,000	$250,000	10 yr.	$226,667		
Modular Furniture	May 2, 2017	S/L	72,000	0	6 yr.	68,000		
Truck	January 25, 2020	DDB	80,000	10,000	8 yr.	45,313		

Analysis component:

_____

_____

_____

_____

Exercise 9-11

Dynamic Exploration Partial Balance Sheet December 31, 2022			

Exercise 9-12

a. Straight-line

	Year 1	Year 2	Year 3	Year 4	Year 5	5-Year Totals
Profit before deprec.						
Deprec. expense						
Profit						

b. Double-declining-balance

	Year 1	Year 2	Year 3	Year 4	Year 5	5-Year Totals
Profit before deprec.						
Deprec. expense						
Profit (loss)						

Analysis component:
_____
_____
_____
_____
_____
_____

Exercise 9-13

Year	Depreciation	
	Straight-Line	Units-of-Production
2021		
2022		
2023		

Analysis component: _____

_____

_____

_____

Exercise 9-14

Year	Depreciation	
	Straight-Line	Double-Declining-Balance
2022		
2023		
2024		

Analysis component: _____

_____

_____

_____

Exercise 9-15

Year	(a)	(b)
	Straight-line	Double-declining balance
2023		
2024		

Name:_____

Exercise 9-16

GENERAL JOURNAL

Page____

Date		Account Titles and Explanation	PR	Debit	Credit

Exercise 9-17 Part 1

GENERAL JOURNAL

Page____

Date		Account Titles and Explanation	PR	Debit	Credit

Part 2

GENERAL JOURNAL

Page____

Date		Account Titles and Explanation	PR	Debit	Credit

Calculations

_____

_____

_____

_____

Name: _____

1. _____

_____

_____

2. _____

_____

_____

Exercise 9-19

GENERAL JOURNAL   Page____

Date		Account Titles and Explanation	PR	Debit	Credit

Calculations:

Exercise 9-20

Part 1   GENERAL JOURNAL   Page____

Date	Account Titles and Explanation	PR	Debit	Credit

Part 2   GENERAL JOURNAL   Page____

Date	Account Titles and Explanation	PR	Debit	Credit

Exercise 9-21

1. _____
_____
_____
_____
_____

2. _____
_____
_____
_____
_____

Exercise 9-22

Part 1   GENERAL JOURNAL   Page____

Date	Account Titles and Explanation	PR	Debit	Credit

Part 2   GENERAL JOURNAL   Page____

Date	Account Titles and Explanation	PR	Debit	Credit

Exercise 9-22 (concluded)

GENERAL JOURNAL   Page____

Date	Account Titles and Explanation	PR	Debit	Credit

Calculations:

Asset	Cost	Accum. Deprec.	Book Value	Recoverable Amount	Impairment Loss	2024 Dep. Exp.
Equipment	$40,000	$20,000		$ 8,000		
Furniture	12,000	9,509		2,950		
Land	85,000	N/A		101,800		
Office Buildng	77,000	23,000		52,500		
Warehouse	55,000	12,938		45,100		

Name: _____

Exercise 9-23

a.   GENERAL JOURNAL   Page____

Date		Account Titles and Explanation	PR	Debit	Credit

b.   GENERAL JOURNAL   Page____

Date		Account Titles and Explanation	PR	Debit	Credit

c.   GENERAL JOURNAL   Page____

Date		Account Titles and Explanation	PR	Debit	Credit

d.   GENERAL JOURNAL   Page____

Date		Account Titles and Explanation	PR	Debit	Credit

Fundamental Accounting Principles, 17ce, Working Papers

Exercise 9-24

To record partial year's depreciation in 2024:

GENERAL JOURNAL Page____

Date		Account Titles and Explanation	PR	Debit	Credit

a. <div align="center">GENERAL JOURNAL</div> Page____

Date		Account Titles and Explanation	PR	Debit	Credit

b. <div align="center">GENERAL JOURNAL</div> Page____

Date		Account Titles and Explanation	PR	Debit	Credit

Exercise 9-25

a. _____
_____

b. _____
_____
_____
_____
_____

c. _____
_____

d.   GENERAL JOURNAL   Page____

Date		Account Titles and Explanation	PR	Debit	Credit

Name:_____

GENERAL JOURNAL   Page____

Date	Account Titles and Explanation	PR	Debit	Credit
a.				
b.				

Analysis component:
_____
_____
_____
_____
_____
_____

Name: _____

Exercise 9-27

GENERAL JOURNAL   Page_____

Date	Account Titles and Explanation	PR	Debit	Credit
a.				
b.				
c.				
d.				

Name:_____

GENERAL JOURNAL   Page____

Date		Account Titles and Explanation	PR	Debit	Credit

Name: _____

1. _____
_____
_____
_____

Part 2   **GENERAL JOURNAL**   Page____

Date	Account Titles and Explanation	PR	Debit	Credit

3. _____
_____
_____
_____
_____
_____
_____

4. _____
_____
_____
_____
_____
_____
_____

GENERAL JOURNAL   Page____

Date	Account Titles and Explanation	PR	Debit	Credit

Exercise 9-30

GENERAL JOURNAL

Page____

Date		Account Titles and Explanation	PR	Debit	Credit

Exercise 9-31

Date	Account Titles and Explanation	PR	Debit	Credit
Part 1.				
Part 2.				

Exercise 9-32

GENERAL JOURNAL Page____

Date	Account Titles and Explanation	PR	Debit	Credit
	Part 1. Disposed at no value			
	Part 2. Sold for $35,000 cash			
	Part 3. Sold for $68,000 cash			
	Part 4. Sold for $80,000 cash			

Balance Sheet			

Calculations

_____

_____ **Balance Sheet**

Calculations

Exercise 9-35

Date	Account Titles and Explanation	PR	Debit	Credit

Name:_____

*Exercise 9-36

Part 1   GENERAL JOURNAL   Page____

Date		Account Titles and Explanation	PR	Debit	Credit

Part 2: _____

Truck:

Component	Date of Purchase	Cost	Est. Resid.	Est. Life	Accum. Dep. at Dec 31/22	Dep. Exp. Dec 31/23	Dep. Exp. Dec 31/24
Truck body	Jul 7/21	$ 28,000	-0-	10 yr	$ 4,200		
Motor	Jul 7/21	8,000	-0-	10 yr	1,200		

Part 3: _____

Problem 9-1A

Part 1

	Land	Building 2	Building 3	Land Improv. 1	Land Improv. 2
Purchase price..........					
Demolition...............					
Landscaping.............					
New building					
New improvements...					
Totals......................					

Calculations:

	Appraised Value	Percent of Total	Apportioned Cost
Land...................................			
Building 2			
Land Improvements 1..............			
Totals.................................			

Part 2

GENERAL JOURNAL Page____

Date	Account Titles and Explanation	PR	Debit	Credit

Name:_____

Problem 9-2A

Derlak Enterprises

Balance Sheet

December 31

	2023		2022	

Analysis component:

_____
_____
_____
_____
_____
_____

Name: _____

Problem 9-3A

Part a.

Year	Straight-Line
2021	
2022	
2023	
2024	
TOTAL	

Part b.

Year	Double-Declining-Balance
2021	
2022	
2023	
2024	
TOTAL	

Part c.

Year	Units-of-Production
2021	
2022	
2023	
2024	
TOTAL	

Chapter 9

Name:_____

Problem 9-4A

Part 1 Purchased January 1, 2023

	2023	2024	2025
A. Double-declining-balance method			
Equipment...................................	$415,000	$415,000	$415,000
Less: Accumulated depreciation............			
Year-end book value........................			
Depreciation expense for the year..........			
B. Straight-line method			
Equipment...................................	$415,000	$415,000	$415,000
Less: Accumulated depreciation............			
Year-end book value........................			
Depreciation expense for the year..........			

Calculations: _____
_____
_____
_____
_____
_____
_____
_____

Name: _____

Problem 9-4A (concluded)

Part 2 Purchased July 1, 2023

	2023	2024	2025
A. Double-declining-balance method			
Equipment.......................................	$415,000	$415,000	$415,000
Less: Accumulated depreciation................			
Year-end book value...................................			
Depreciation expense for the year........................			
B. Straight-line method			
Equipment...	$415,000	$415,000	$415,000
Less: Accumulated depreciation................			
Year-end book value...................................			
Depreciation expense for the year........................			

Calculations:

_____
_____
_____
_____
_____
_____
_____
_____

　　　　　　　　　　　　　　Name:_____

Problem 9-5A

Year	Depreciation Method		
	Straight-Line	Double-Declining-Balance	Units-of-Production
2023			
2024			
2025			

Analysis component:

_____
_____
_____
_____
_____
_____
_____
_____
_____
_____

Name: _____

Problem 9-6A

Year	Depreciation Method:		
	Straight-line	Double-declining-balance	Units-of-production
2023			
2024			
2025			

Calculations:

1. Double-declining-balance method   <u>2023</u>   <u>2024</u>   <u>2025</u>
   Equipment...
   Less: Accumulated depreciation............
   Year-end book value.............................
   Depreciation expense for the year...........

2. Straight-line method   <u>2023</u>   <u>2024</u>   <u>2025</u>
   Equipment ....
   Less: Accumulated depreciation............
   Year-end book value ....
   Depreciation expense for the year ....

Problem 9-7A

Part 1

GENERAL JOURNAL   Page____

Date		Account Titles and Explanation	PR	Debit	Credit

Part 2

Big Sky Farms
Partial Balance Sheet
April 30, 2024

Problem 9-8A

Part 1

	Market Value	Percentage of Total	Apportioned Cost
Building	_____	_____	_____
Land.................................	_____	_____	_____
Land improvements..............	_____	_____	_____
Vehicles.............................	_____	_____	_____
Total.................................	═══════	═══════	═══════

GENERAL JOURNAL   Page____

Date	Account Titles and Explanation	PR	Debit	Credit

Part 2: 2023 straight-line depreciation on building:

_____

_____

_____

Part 3: 2023 double-declining-balance depreciation on land improvements:

_____

_____

_____

Analysis component:

_____

_____

_____

_____

_____

_____

_____

Problem 9-9A

| Year | Depreciation | | |
	Straight-Line	Units-of-Production	Double-Declining-Balance
2023			
2024			
2025			
2026			
2027			
Totals			

Calculations:

Problem 9-10A

Description	Cost Information						Depreciation		
	Date of Purchase	Depreciation Method	Cost	Residual	Life	Balance of Accum. Deprec. Dec. 31, 2023	Balance of Accum. Deprec. Dec. 31, 2023	Depreciation Expense for 2024	Balance of Accum. Deprec. Dec. 31, 2024
Office equipment	March 27/20	Straight-line	$52,000	$14,000	10 yr.				
Machinery	June 4/20	Double-declining-balance	275,000	46,000	6 yr.				
Truck	Nov. 13/23	Units-of-production	113,000	26,000	250,000 km.				

Calculations:

Problem 9-11A

GENERAL JOURNAL   Page____

Date	Account Titles and Explanation	PR	Debit	Credit

Calculations:

Problem 9-12A

GENERAL JOURNAL   Page____

Date	Account Titles and Explanation	PR	Debit	Credit

Calculations:

Problem 9-13A

Part 1: Entry to record the purchase of the replacement blade:

GENERAL JOURNAL

Page____

Date		Account Titles and Explanation	PR	Debit	Credit

Calculations:

Part 2:
Total depreciation expense to be recorded on Machine #5027 for 2023:_____

Calculations:

Problem 9-14A

Part 1   **GENERAL JOURNAL**   Page____

Date		Account Titles and Explanation	PR	Debit	Credit

Calculations:

	Book Value	Recoverable Value	Impairment Loss
Land		$136,400	
Building		105,600	
Equipment		28,600	
Furniture		15,400	

Problem 9-14A (continued)

Part 2

Problem 9-14A (concl'd.)

Analysis component:

_____

_____
_____
_____
_____
_____
_____
_____
_____
_____
_____

Problem 9-15A

Part 1   **GENERAL JOURNAL**   Page____

Date		Account Titles and Explanation	PR	Debit	Credit

Calculations:

Problem 9-15A (concl'd.)

Part 2   **GENERAL JOURNAL**   Page____

Date		Account Titles and Explanation	PR	Debit	Credit

Calculations:

Problem 9-16A

Part 1   **GENERAL JOURNAL**   Page____

Date		Account Titles and Explanation	PR	Debit	Credit

Part 2   **GENERAL JOURNAL**   Page____

Date		Account Titles and Explanation	PR	Debit	Credit

Problem 9-16A (concl'd.)

Part 3(a)   **GENERAL JOURNAL**   Page____

Date	Account Titles and Explanation	PR	Debit	Credit

Part 3(b)   **GENERAL JOURNAL**   Page____

Date	Account Titles and Explanation	PR	Debit	Credit

Part 3(c)   **GENERAL JOURNAL**   Page____

Date	Account Titles and Explanation	PR	Debit	Credit

Calculations:

Name: _____

Problem 9-17A

GENERAL JOURNAL

Page____

Date	Account Titles and Explanation	PR	Debit	Credit

Calculations:

Problem 9-18A

a. Depreciation expense on first December 31 of each machine's life:

GENERAL JOURNAL   Page____

Date	Account Titles and Explanation	PR	Debit	Credit

b. Purchase/exchange/disposal of each machine:

GENERAL JOURNAL   Page____

Date	Account Titles and Explanation	PR	Debit	Credit

Problem 9-18A (concl'd.)

GENERAL JOURNAL

Page_____

Date		Account Titles and Explanation	PR	Debit	Credit

Calculations:

Problem 9-19A

a.   GENERAL JOURNAL   Page____

Date	Account Titles and Explanation	PR	Debit	Credit

b.   GENERAL JOURNAL   Page____

Date	Account Titles and Explanation	PR	Debit	Credit

Problem 9-20A

Part 1   GENERAL JOURNAL   Page____

Date	Account Titles and Explanation	PR	Debit	Credit

Problem 9-20A (concl'd.)

Part 2   GENERAL JOURNAL   Page____

Date	Account Titles and Explanation	PR	Debit	Credit

Problem 9-21A

GENERAL JOURNAL

Date	Account Titles and Explanation	PR	Debit	Credit

Calculations:

*Problem 9-22A

1a.   GENERAL JOURNAL   Page____

Date	Account Titles and Explanation	PR	Debit	Credit

1b.   GENERAL JOURNAL   Page____

Date	Account Titles and Explanation	PR	Debit	Credit

Calculations:

Part 2

_____
_____
_____
_____
_____
_____

Problem 9-1B

Part 1

	Land	Building B	Building C	Land Improv. B	Land Improv. C
Purchase price............					
Demolition..................					
Landscaping...............					
New building					
New improvements					
Totals.........................					

Calculations:

Allocation of purchase price:

	Appraised Value	*Percent of Total*	*Apportioned Cost*
Land..	$317,034		
Building B..................................	189,108		
Land Improvements B	50,058		
Totals...	$556,200	100 %	$540,000

Part 2

GENERAL JOURNAL   Page____

Date	Account Titles and Explanation	PR	Debit	Credit

Name: _____

Problem 9-2B

	Xentel Interactive			
	Balance Sheet			
	September 30			
	2023		2022	

Fundamental Accounting Principles, 17ce, Working Papers

Problem 9-2B (concl'd.)

Analysis component: _____

_____

_____

_____

_____

_____

_____

_____

Problem 9-3B

Part a.

Year	Straight-Line
2021	
2022	
2023	
2024	
TOTAL	

Part b.

Year	Double-Declining-Balance
2021	
2022	
2023	
2024	
TOTAL	

Name: _____

Problem 9-3B (concl'd.)

Part c.

Year	Units-of-Production
2021	
2022	
2023	
2024	
TOTAL	

Part d.

_____

_____

_____

_____

_____

_____

Chapter 9

Name:_____

Problem 9-4B

Part 1 Purchased January 1

	2023	2024	2025
A. Double-declining balance method			
Machinery	$588,000	$588,000	$588,000
Less: Accumulated depreciation	------	------	------
Year-end book value	------	------	------
Depreciation expense for the year	------	------	------
B. Straight-line method			
Machinery	$588,000	$588,000	$588,000
Less: Accumulated depreciation	------	------	------
Year-end book value	------	------	------
Depreciation expense for the year	------	------	------

Part 2 Purchased April 1

	2023	2024	2025
A. Double-declining balance method			
Machinery	$588,000	$588,000	$588,000
Less: Accumulated depreciation	------	------	------
Year-end book value	------	------	------
Depreciation expense for the year	------	------	------
B. Straight-line method			
Machinery	$588,000	$588,000	$588,000
Less: Accumulated depreciation	------	------	------
Year-end book value	------	------	------
Depreciation expense for the year	------	------	------

Problem 9-5B

Year	Depreciation Method		
	Straight-Line	Double-Declining-Balance	Units-of-Production
2023			
2024			
2025			
2026			
2027			
2028			
Totals			

Problem 9-6B

Year	Depreciation Method		
	Straight-Line	**Double-Declining-Balance**	**Units-of-Production**
2023			
2024			
2025			
2026			
2027			
2028			
Totals			

Calculations:

Chapter 9

Name: _____

Problem 9-7B

Part 1

GENERAL JOURNAL   Page____

Date		Account Titles and Explanation	PR	Debit	Credit

Part 2

Westfair Foods
Partial Balance Sheet
December 31, 2024

Problem 9-8B

Part 1

	Market Value	Percentage of Total	Apportioned Cost
Building			
Land..................................			
Land improvements..............			
Truck.................................	_____	_____	_____
Total..................................			
	════	════	════

GENERAL JOURNAL   Page____

Date	Account Titles and Explanation	PR	Debit	Credit

Part 2: 2023 straight-line depreciation on building:

_____

_____

_____

Part 3: 2023 double-declining-balance depreciation on land improvements:

_____

_____

_____

Problem 9-9B

Year	Depreciation		
	Straight-Line	**Units-of-Production**	**Double-Declining-Balance**
2023			
2024			
2025			
2026			
2027			
2028			
Totals			

Calculations:

Fundamental Accounting Principles, 17ce, Working Papers

Problem 9-10B

Cost Information						Depreciation		
Description	Date of Purchase	Depreciation Method	Cost	Residual	Life	Balance of Accum. Deprec. Apr. 30, 2023	Depreciation Expense for 2024	Balance of Accum. Deprec. Apr. 30, 2024
Equipment	Oct. 3/20	Straight-line	$62,400	$16,800	20 yr.			
Machinery	Oct. 28/20	Units-of-production	540,000	180,000	100,000 units			
Tools	Nov. 3/20	Double-declining-balance	64,000	15,000	5 yr.			

Calculations:

Problem 9-11B

GENERAL JOURNAL

Date	Account Titles and Explanation	PR	Debit	Credit

Calculations:

Name:_____

Problem 9-12B

GENERAL JOURNAL

Page____

Date	Account Titles and Explanation	PR	Debit	Credit

Calculations:

Problem 9-13B

Part 1: Entry to record the purchase of the new furnace:

GENERAL JOURNAL   Page____

Date	Account Titles and Explanation	PR	Debit	Credit

Calculations:

Part 2:
Total depreciation expense to be recorded on the warehouse for 2023:_____

Calculations:

Windows		
Doors		
Roofing		
Siding		
Framing/Walls		
Furnace		
Misc.		
Total depreciation expense to be recorded on the warehouse for 2023		

Problem 9-14B

Part 1

GENERAL JOURNAL

Page____

Date	Account Titles and Explanation	PR	Debit	Credit

Calculations:

	Book Value	Recoverable Value	Impairment Loss
Computer equipment		$ 6,250	
Land		172,500	
Machinery		65,000	
Warehouse		243,750	

Name: _____

Problem 9-14B (cont'd.)

Part 2

_____

Analysis component:

_____
_____
_____
_____
_____
_____
_____

Problem 9-15B

Part 1

GENERAL JOURNAL

Date		Account Titles and Explanation	PR	Debit	Credit

Calculations:

Problem 9-15B (cont'd.)

Part 2   **GENERAL JOURNAL**   Page____

Date		Account Titles and Explanation	PR	Debit	Credit

Calculations:

Problem 9-15B (concl'd.)

Part 3   **GENERAL JOURNAL**   Page____

Date		Account Titles and Explanation	PR	Debit	Credit

Calculations:

Name: _____

Problem 9-16B

Part 1   GENERAL JOURNAL   Page____

Date	Account Titles and Explanation	PR	Debit	Credit

Part 2   GENERAL JOURNAL   Page____

Date	Account Titles and Explanation	PR	Debit	Credit

Problem 9-16B (concl'd.)

Part 3(a)   GENERAL JOURNAL   Page____

Date		Account Titles and Explanation	PR	Debit	Credit

Part 3(b)   GENERAL JOURNAL   Page____

Date		Account Titles and Explanation	PR	Debit	Credit

Part 3(c)   GENERAL JOURNAL   Page____

Date		Account Titles and Explanation	PR	Debit	Credit

Calculations:

Problem 9-17B

		GENERAL JOURNAL			Page____

Date		Account Titles and Explanation	PR	Debit	Credit

Calculations:

Problem 9-18B

1. Depreciation expense on first December 31 of each machine's life:

GENERAL JOURNAL **Page____**

Date		Account Titles and Explanation	PR	Debit	Credit

2. Purchase/exchange/disposal of each machine:

GENERAL JOURNAL **Page____**

Date		Account Titles and Explanation	PR	Debit	Credit

Problem 9-18B (concl'd.)

GENERAL JOURNAL

Page_____

Date	Account Titles and Explanation	PR	Debit	Credit

Calculations:

Name:_____

Problem 9-19B

1a.   GENERAL JOURNAL   Page____

Date		Account Titles and Explanation	PR	Debit	Credit

1b.   GENERAL JOURNAL   Page____

Date		Account Titles and Explanation	PR	Debit	Credit

Part 2

Partial Balance Sheet			

Problem 9-20B

Part 1 **GENERAL JOURNAL** Page____

Date	Account Titles and Explanation	PR	Debit	Credit

Part 2 **GENERAL JOURNAL** Page____

Date	Account Titles and Explanation	PR	Debit	Credit

*Problem 9-21B

| GENERAL JOURNAL | | | | Page____ |

*Problem 9-21B

GENERAL JOURNAL   Page____

Date	Account Titles and Explanation	PR	Debit	Credit

Calculations

Name: _____

*Problem 9-22B

1a. GENERAL JOURNAL Page____

Date		Account Titles and Explanation	PR	Debit	Credit

1b. GENERAL JOURNAL Page____

Date		Account Titles and Explanation	PR	Debit	Credit

Calculations:

Name:_____

*Problem 9-22B (concl'd.)

Part 2

Metal Frame		
Engine	2018:	
	2019:	
	2020:	
	2021:	
	2022:	
	2023:	
New Fan		
Conveyor System		
Misc. Parts	2018:	
	2019:	
	2020:	
	2021:	
	2022:	
	Total	

Quick Study AI-1

_____

_____
_____
_____
_____

Quick Study AI-2

GENERAL JOURNAL

Date	Account Titles and Explanation	PR	Debit	Credit

Quick Study AI-3

GENERAL JOURNAL

Date	Account Titles and Explanation	PR	Debit	Credit

Quick Study AI-4

		Deductions				Pay	Distribution	
Employee	Gross Pay	EI Premium	Income Taxes	CPP	Deductions Total	Net Pay	Office Salaries	Sales Salaries
Johnson, S.	1,200.00	18.97	303.85	61.74				
Waverley, N.	530.00	8.37	123.05	25.22				
Zender, B.	675.00	10.67	156.75	33.12				
Totals	2,405.00	38.01	583.65	120.08				

Quick Study AI-5

| Employee | Gross Pay | Deductions | | | | Pay | Salaries Expense |
		EI Premium	Income Taxes	CPP	Total Deductions	Net Pay	
Bentley, A.	2,010.00						
Craig, T.	2,115.00						
Totals	4,125.00						

Quick Study AI-6

| Employee | Gross Pay | Deductions | | | | Pay | Distribution | |
		EI Premium	Income Taxes	CPP	Total Deductions	Net Pay	Office Salaries	Sales Salaries
Withers, S.	2,500.00						2,500.00	
Volt, C.	1,800.00							1,800.00
Totals								

Calculations:

_____
_____
_____
_____
_____
_____
_____
_____
_____

Quick Study AI-7

GENERAL JOURNAL   Page____

Date	Account Titles and Explanation	PR	Debit	Credit

Name:_____

Quick Study AI-8

GENERAL JOURNAL

Date		Account Titles and Explanation	PR	Debit	Credit

Quick Study AI-9

GENERAL JOURNAL

Date		Account Titles and Explanation	PR	Debit	Credit

Quick Study AI-10

GENERAL JOURNAL

Date		Account Titles and Explanation	PR	Debit	Credit

Quick Study AI-11

GENERAL JOURNAL

Date		Account Titles and Explanation	PR	Debit	Credit

Exercise AI-1

Exercise AI-2

Employee	Gross Pay	EI Premium	Income Taxes	CPP	Health Insurance Deductions	Total Deductions	Net Pay
H. Craig	720.00		168.10		24.00		
J. Lim	610.00		142.05		24.00		
D. Patelli	830.00		194.65		36.00		
S. McFee	1,700.00		468.65		24.00		
Totals	3,860.00		973.45		108.00		

Calculations:

Exercise AI-2 (concl'd.)

GENERAL JOURNAL

Date	Account Titles and Explanation	PR	Debit	Credit

Exercise AI-3

Employee	Gross Pay	Deductions					Pay	Distribution	
		EI Prem.	Income Taxes	United Way	CPP	Total Deductions	Net Pay	Admin. Salaries	Sales Salaries
Atkins, D.	1,900.00	30.02	449.95	80.00	96.21				
Nesbitt, M.	1,260.00	19.91	293.30	50.00	61.33				
Trent, F.	1,680.00	26.54	392.90	40.00	84.22				
Vallot, M.	3,000.00	47.40	805.45	300.00	156.16				
Totals	7,840.00	123.87	1,941.60	470.00	397.92				

Exercise AI-4

Employee	Gross Pay	Deductions						Pay	Distribution	
		EI Prem.	Income Taxes	Canada Savings Bonds	CPP	United Way	Total Deductions	Net Pay	Office Salaries	Sales Salaries
Crimson	1,995.00								1,995.00	
Long	2,040.00									2,040.00
Morris	2,000.00									2,000.00
Peterson	2,280.00									2,280.00
Totals	8,315.00									

Appendix I

Name:_____

Exercise AI-5

Employee	Gross Pay	EI Prem.	Income Taxes	Medical Ins.	CPP	United Way	Total Deductions	Net Pay	Office Salaries	Guide Salaries
								Payment	**Distribution**	
Wynn	1,200.00			65.00		40.00				1,200.00
Short	950.00			65.00		100.00			950.00	
Pearl	1,150.00			65.00		0				1,150.00
Quincy	875.00			65.00		50.00				875.00
Totals	4,175.00									

Calculations:

_____
_____
_____
_____
_____
_____
_____
_____
_____
_____
_____

Exercise AI-6

GENERAL JOURNAL

Date	Account Titles and Explanation	PR	Debit	Credit

Name:_____

Exercise AI-7

GENERAL JOURNAL

Date		Account Titles and Explanation	PR	Debit	Credit

Exercise AI-8

GENERAL JOURNAL

Date		Account Titles and Explanation	PR	Debit	Credit

Exercise AI-9

GENERAL JOURNAL

Date		Account Titles and Explanation	PR	Debit	Credit

Exercise AI-10

GENERAL JOURNAL

Date		Account Titles and Explanation	PR	Debit	Credit

Exercise AI-11

Employee	CPP Contribution	EI Contribution	Retirement Fund Contributions	Health Insurance

Calculations:

_____
_____
_____
_____
_____
_____
_____
_____
_____
_____
_____

Name:_____

Exercise AI-12

GENERAL JOURNAL

Date		Account Titles and Explanation	PR	Debit	Credit

Exercise AI-13

GENERAL JOURNAL

Date		Account Titles and Explanation	PR	Debit	Credit

Problem AI-1A

Part 1

| Employee | Daily Time | | | | | | | Total Hrs. | O.T. Hrs. | Reg. Pay Rate | Earnings | | |
	M	T	W	T	F	S	S				Regular Pay	O.T. Premium Pay	Gross Pay
Loran	8	8	8	8	8	4	0			40.00			
Sousa	7	8	6	7	8	4	0			36.00			
Smith	8	8	0	8	8	4	4			32.00			
Parton	8	8	8	8	8	0	0			40.00			
Wood	0	6	6	6	6	8	8			36.00			

| Employee | Deductions | | | | | | Payment | Distribution | |
	EI Prem.	CPP	Income Tax	Hosp. Ins.	Union Dues	Total Deductions	Net Pay	Office Wages Expense	Service Wages Expense
Loran				40.00	16.00				
Sousa				40.00	15.00				
Smith				40.00	14.00				
Parton				40.00	16.00				
Wood				40.00	16.00				
Totals				200.00	77.00				

Part 2

GENERAL JOURNAL

Date		Account Titles and Explanation	PR	Debit	Credit

Problem AI-2A

Part 1

GENERAL JOURNAL

Date		Account Titles and Explanation	PR	Debit	Credit

Part 2

GENERAL JOURNAL

Date		Account Titles and Explanation	PR	Debit	Credit

Problem AI-3A

Part 1

GENERAL JOURNAL

Date		Account Titles and Explanation	PR	Debit	Credit

Problem AI-3A (concl.)

Part 2

GENERAL JOURNAL

Date		Account Titles and Explanation	PR	Debit	Credit

Part 3

GENERAL JOURNAL

Date		Account Titles and Explanation	PR	Debit	Credit

Problem AI-4A

GENERAL JOURNAL

Date		Account Titles and Explanation	PR	Debit	Credit

Problem AI-4A (concl.)

GENERAL JOURNAL

Date	Account Titles and Explanation	PR	Debit	Credit

Fundamental Accounting Principles, 17ce, Working Papers

Problem AI-1B

Part 1

Employee	M	T	W	T	F	S	S	Total Hrs.	O.T. Hrs.	Reg. Pay Rate	Regular Pay	O.T. Premium Pay	Gross Pay
			Daily Time									Earnings	
Amoko	8	8	8	8	8	0	0			34.00			
Carson	7	8	8	7	8	4	0			36.00			
Cheng	8	8	0	8	8	4	4			36.00			
Deszca	8	8	8	8	8	0	0			30.00			
Tan	0	6	6	6	6	8	8			30.00			

Employee	EI Prem.	CPP	Income Tax	Hosp. Ins.	Union Dues	Total Deductions	Net Pay	Office Wages Expense	Service Wages Expense
			Deductions				Payment	Distribution	
Amoko				30.00	12.00				
Carson				30.00	12.00				
Cheng				30.00	12.00				
Deszca				30.00	12.00				
Tan				30.00	12.00				
Totals				150.00	60.00				

Part 2

GENERAL JOURNAL

Date	Account Titles and Explanation	PR	Debit	Credit

Name:_____

Problem AI-2B

Part 1

GENERAL JOURNAL

Date		Account Titles and Explanation	PR	Debit	Credit

Part 2

GENERAL JOURNAL

Date		Account Titles and Explanation	PR	Debit	Credit

Problem AI-3B

Part 1

GENERAL JOURNAL

Date		Account Titles and Explanation	PR	Debit	Credit

Problem AI-3B (concl.)

Part 2

GENERAL JOURNAL

Date		Account Titles and Explanation	PR	Debit	Credit

Part 3

GENERAL JOURNAL

Date		Account Titles and Explanation	PR	Debit	Credit

Problem AI-4B

GENERAL JOURNAL

Date		Account Titles and Explanation	PR	Debit	Credit

Problem AI-4B(concl.)

GENERAL JOURNAL

Date		Account Titles and Explanation	PR	Debit	Credit

Appendix II   Name: _____

Quick Study AII-1

1. _____	3. _____
2. _____	4. _____

Quick Study AII-2

1. _____	5. _____
2. _____	6. _____
3. _____	7. _____
4. _____	8. _____

Quick Study AII-3

1. _____	6. _____
2. _____	7. _____
3. _____	8. _____
4. _____	9. _____
5. _____	10. _____

Quick Study AII-4

a. _____	e. _____
b. _____	f. _____
c. _____	g. _____
d. _____	

Quick Study AII-5

a. _____	d. _____
b. _____	e. _____
c. _____	f. _____

Quick Study AII-6

	GENERAL JOURNAL				Page_____
Date	Account Titles and Explanation	PR	Debit	Credit

Quick Study AII-7

1. _____	5. _____
2. _____	6. _____
3. _____	7. _____
4. _____	

Quick Study AII-8

		Sales Journal			Page
Date	Account Debited	Invoice Number	PR	Accounts Receivable Dr. Sales Cr.	Cost of Goods Sold Dr. Merchandise Inventory Cr.

Quick Study AII-9

1. _____	5. _____
2. _____	6. _____
3. _____	7. _____
4. _____	

Quick Study AII-10

		Cash Receipts Journal							Page
Date	Account Credited	Explanation	PR	Cash Dr.	Sales Disc. Dr.	Accts. Rec. Cr.	Sales Cr.	Other Accts. Cr.	COGS Dr. Merch. Inv. Cr.

Quick Study AII-11

						Purchases Journal			Page
Date	Account	Date of Invoice	Terms	PR		Accounts Payable Cr.	Merch. Inventory Dr.	Office Supplies Dr.	Other Accounts Dr.

Quick Study AII-12

_____

_____

_____

_____

_____

_____

_____

_____

Quick Study AII-13

a. _____	e. _____
b. _____	f. _____
c. _____	g. _____
d. _____	h. _____

Quick Study AII-14

				Sales Journal	Page
Date	Account Debited	Invoice Number	PR	Accounts Receivable Dr. Sales Cr.	Cost of Goods Sold Dr. Merchandise Inventory Cr.

Quick Study AII-15

a. _____	d. _____
b. _____	e. _____
c. _____	f. _____

Quick Study AII-16

								Page
			Cash Payments Journal					
Date	Chq No.	Payee	Account Debited	PR	Cash Cr.	Inventory Cr.	Other Accounts Dr.	Accounts Payable Dr.

Quick Study AII-17

GENERAL JOURNAL   Page____

Date	Account Titles and Explanation	PR	Debit	Credit

Exercise AII-1

				Sales Journal		Page
Date	Account Debited	Invoice Number	PR	Accounts Receivable Dr. Sales Cr.		Cost of Goods Sold Dr. Merchandise Inventory Cr.

Exercise AII-2

				Cash Receipts Journal						Page
Date	Account Credited	PR	Explanation	Cash Dr.	Sales Disc. Dr.	Accts. Rec. Cr.	Sales Cr.	Other Accts. Cr.	COGS Dr. Merch. Inv. Cr.

Exercise AII-3

				Cash Receipts Journal						Page
Date	Account Credited	Explanation	PR	Cash Dr.	Sales Disc. Dr.	Accts. Rec. Cr.	Sales Cr.	Other Accts. Cr.	COGS Dr. Merch. Inv. Cr.

Appendix II

Exercise AII-4

					Purchases Journal			Page	
Date	Account Credited	Date of Invoice	Terms	PR	Accts. Payable Cr.	Purchases Dr.	Office Supplies Dr.	Other Accts. Dr.	

Exercise AII-5

					Cash Disbursements Journal			Page	
Date	Ch. No.	Payee	Account Debited	PR	Cash Cr.	Merch. Inventory Cr.	Other Accounts Dr.	Accounts Payable Dr.	

Exercise AII-6

Part 1 – Wilson Purchasing

					Purchases Journal			Page
Date	Account Credited	Date of Invoice	Terms	PR	Accounts Payable Cr.	Merch. Inventory Dr.	Office Supplies Dr.	Other Accounts Dr.

					Cash Disbursements Journal			Page
Date	Ch. No.	Payee	Account Debited	PR	Cash Cr.	Merch. Inventory Cr.	Other Accounts Dr.	Accounts Payable Dr.

GENERAL JOURNAL   Page____

Date		Account Titles and Explanation	PR	Debit	Credit

Exercise AII-6 (concl'd.)

Part 2 – Hostel Sales

Sales Journal					Page
Date	Account Debited	Invoice Number	PR	Accounts Receivable Dr. Sales Cr.	Cost of Goods Sold Dr. Merchandise Inventory Cr.

Cash Receipts Journal									Page
Date	Accounts Credited	PR	Explanation	Cash Dr.	Sales Disc. Dr.	Accts. Rec. Cr.	Sales Cr.	Other Accts. Cr.	COGS Dr. Merch. Inv. Cr.

GENERAL JOURNAL   Page____

Date		Account Titles and Explanation	PR	Debit	Credit

Name: _____

Exercise AII-7

Part 1 – Wilson Purchasing

Purchases Journal								Page
Date	Account Credited	Date of Invoice	Terms	PR	Accts. Payable Cr.	Purchases Dr.	Office Supplies Dr.	Other Accts. Dr.

Cash Disbursements Journal								Page
Date	Ch. No.	Payee	Account Debited	PR	Cash Cr.	Purch. Disc. Cr.	Other Accounts Dr.	Accts. Payable Dr.

GENERAL JOURNAL

Page____

Date		Account Titles and Explanation	PR	Debit	Credit

Exercise AII-7 (concl'd.)

Part 2 – Hostel Sales

Sales Journal				Page
Date	Account Debited	Invoice No.	PR	Accounts Receivable Dr. Sales Cr.

Cash Receipts Journal								Page
Date	Account Credited	Explanation	PR	Cash Dr.	Sales Disc. Dr.	Accts. Rec. Cr.	Sales Cr.	Other Accts. Cr.

GENERAL JOURNAL   Page____

Date		Account Titles and Explanation	PR	Debit	Credit

Name: _____

Exercise AII-8

_____
_____
_____
_____
_____
_____
_____
_____
_____
_____
_____
_____
_____

Exercise AII-9

a. _____

b. _____

c. _____

d. _____

e. _____

Fundamental Accounting Principles, 17ce, Working Papers

Exercise AII-10

Part 1   **ACCOUNTS RECEIVABLE SUBLEDGER**

Sanders Farrell	Dan Holland	Brad Smithers

Part 2   **GENERAL LEDGER**

Accounts Receivable	Sales	Sales Returns and Allowances

Part 3

Schedule of Accounts Receivable

Accounts Receivable Controlling Account

Exercise AII-11

Part 1   ACCOUNTS PAYABLE SUBLEDGER

Bailey Company

DATE	EXPLANATION	PR	DEBIT	CREDIT	BALANCE

Johnson Brothers

DATE	EXPLANATION	PR	DEBIT	CREDIT	BALANCE

Preston Company

DATE	EXPLANATION	PR	DEBIT	CREDIT	BALANCE

Part 2   GENERAL LEDGER

Accounts Payable

DATE	EXPLANATION	PR	DEBIT	CREDIT	BALANCE

Exercise AII-12

Sales Journal					Page
Date	Account Debited	Invoice Number	PR	Accounts Receivable Dr. Sales Cr.	Cost of Goods Sold Dr. Merchandise Inventory Cr.

Exercise AII-13

				Cash Receipts Journal				Page
Date	Account Credited	Explanation	PR	Cash Dr.	Sales Disc. Dr.	Accts. Rec. Cr.	Sales Cr.	Other Accts. Cr.

Exercise AII-14

					Purchases Journal			Page
Date	Account	Date of Invoice	Terms	PR	Accounts Payable Cr.	Merch. Inventory Dr.	Office Supplies Dr.	Other Accounts Dr.

GENERAL LEDGER		
Cash	**Accounts Payable**	**Sales Returns and Allowances**
Accts. Receivable	**Notes Payable**	**Purchases**
Prepaid Insurance	**Sales**	**Purchase Discounts**
Store Equipment	**Sales Discounts**	**Purchase Returns and Allowances**

ACCOUNTS RECEIVABLE SUBLEDGER		
Jack Hertz	**Trudy Stone**	**Dave Waylon**

ACCOUNTS PAYABLE SUBLEDGER		
Grass Corp.	**McGrew Company**	**Sulter Inc.**

Problem AII-1A

Special Journal		Subledger	
Sales.................................	S	Accounts Receivable	AR
Purchases.......................	P	Accounts Payable.............	AP
Cash Receipts.................	CR	Merchandise Inventory....	MI
Cash Payments..............	CD	No Effect.........................	NE
General Journal.............	G		

Date	Transaction	Special Journal	Subledger
Mar. 1	*Sold merchandise on credit.*	*S*	*AR/MI*
2	Defective merchandise sold on March 1 was returned by the customer. It was scrapped.		
3	Purchased office equipment on credit; terms n/30.		
5	Received payment regarding the March 1 sale.		
10	Received a credit memo from the supplier regarding defective equipment purchased on March 3.		
14	Sold merchandise for cash.		
16	Purchased merchandise inventory on credit; terms 1/5, n/30.		
17	Paid the balance owing on the March 3 transaction.		
18	Purchased merchandise inventory for cash.		
21	Paid for the merchandise purchased on March 16.		
22	Sold old equipment for cash.		
30	Paid salaries for the month of March.		
30	Accrued utilities for the month of March.		
30	Closed the credit balance in the Income Summary to Capital.		

Problem AII-2A

				Sales Journal		Page 3
Date	Account Debited	Invoice Number	PR	Accounts Receivable Dr. Sales Cr.		Cost of Goods Sold Dr. Merchandise Inventory Cr.

							Cash Receipts Journal		Page 3
Date	Account Credited	PR	Explanation	Cash Dr.	Sales Disc. Dr.	Accts. Rec. Cr.	Sales Cr.	Other Accts. Cr.	COGS Dr. Merch. Inv. Cr.

					Purchases Journal			Page 3
Date	Account Credited	Date of Invoice	Terms	PR	Accounts Payable Cr.	Merch. Inventory Dr.	Office Supplies Dr.	Other Accounts Dr.

					Cash Disbursements Journal			Page 3
Date	Ch. No.	Payee	Account Debited	PR	Cash Cr.	Merch. Inventory Cr.	Other Accounts Dr.	Accounts Payable Dr.

Problem AII-2A (concl'd.)

GENERAL JOURNAL
Page____

Date		Account Titles and Explanation	PR	Debit	Credit

Problem AII-3A   Part 1

ACCOUNTS RECEIVABLE SUBLEDGER

Paul Abrams

ACCOUNT NO. 106-1

DATE	EXPLANATION	PR	DEBIT	CREDIT	BALANCE

Linda Hobart

ACCOUNT NO. 106-2

DATE	EXPLANATION	PR	DEBIT	CREDIT	BALANCE

Kelly Schaefer

ACCOUNT NO. 106-3

DATE	EXPLANATION	PR	DEBIT	CREDIT	BALANCE

Name: _____

Problem AII-3A (cont'd.)

Part 2   ACCOUNTS PAYABLE SUBLEDGER

Frank's Supply   ACCOUNT NO. 201-1

DATE	EXPLANATION	PR	DEBIT	CREDIT	BALANCE

Baskin Company   ACCOUNT NO. 201-2

DATE	EXPLANATION	PR	DEBIT	CREDIT	BALANCE

Sprocket Company   ACCOUNT NO. 201-3

DATE	EXPLANATION	PR	DEBIT	CREDIT	BALANCE

Eau Claire Inc.   ACCOUNT NO. 201-4

DATE	EXPLANATION	PR	DEBIT	CREDIT	BALANCE

Problem AII-3A (cont'd.)

Part 3

				Sales Journal		Page 3
Date	Account Debited	Invoice Number	PR	Accounts Receivable Dr. Sales Cr.		Cost of Goods Sold Dr. Merchandise Inventory Cr.

				Cash Receipts Journal					Page 3
Date	Accounts Credited	PR	Explanation	Cash Dr.	Sales Disc. Dr.	Accts. Rec. Cr.	Sales Cr.	Other Accts. Cr.	COGS Dr. Merch. Inv. Cr.

Problem AII-3A (concl'd.)

					Purchases Journal			Page 3
Date	Account Credited	Date of Invoice	Terms	PR	Accounts Payable Cr.	Merch. Inventory Dr.	Office Supplies Dr.	Other Accounts Dr.

					Cash Disbursements Journal			Page 3
Date	Ch. No.	Payee	Account Debited	PR	Cash Cr.	Merch. Inventory Cr.	Other Accounts Dr.	Accounts Payable Dr.

GENERAL JOURNAL   Page____

Date		Account Titles and Explanation	PR	Debit	Credit

Problem AII-4A Parts 1, 4

GENERAL LEDGER

Cash   ACCOUNT NO. 101

DATE	EXPLANATION	PR	DEBIT	CREDIT	BALANCE
2023					
Mar.31	Balance brought forward				167,000

Accounts Receivable   ACCOUNT NO. 106

DATE	EXPLANATION	PR	DEBIT	CREDIT	BALANCE

Merchandise Inventory   ACCOUNT NO. 119

DATE	EXPLANATION	PR	DEBIT	CREDIT	BALANCE
2023					
Mar.31	Balance brought forward				105,000

Office Supplies   ACCOUNT NO. 124

DATE	EXPLANATION	PR	DEBIT	CREDIT	BALANCE

Store Supplies   ACCOUNT NO. 125

DATE	EXPLANATION	PR	DEBIT	CREDIT	BALANCE

Store Equipment   ACCOUNT NO. 165

DATE	EXPLANATION	PR	DEBIT	CREDIT	BALANCE

Problem AII-4A (cont'd)

Accounts Payable — ACCOUNT NO. 201

DATE	EXPLANATION	PR	DEBIT	CREDIT	BALANCE

Long-Term Notes Payable — ACCOUNT NO. 251

DATE	EXPLANATION	PR	DEBIT	CREDIT	BALANCE
2023					
Mar.31	Balance brought forward				167,000

Jeff Newton, Capital — ACCOUNT NO. 301

DATE	EXPLANATION	PR	DEBIT	CREDIT	BALANCE
2023					
Mar.31	Balance brought forward				105,000

Sales — ACCOUNT NO. 413

DATE	EXPLANATION	PR	DEBIT	CREDIT	BALANCE

Sales Discounts — ACCOUNT NO. 415

DATE	EXPLANATION	PR	DEBIT	CREDIT	BALANCE

Cost of Goods Sold — ACCOUNT NO. 502

DATE	EXPLANATION	PR	DEBIT	CREDIT	BALANCE

Sales Salaries Expense — ACCOUNT NO. 621

DATE	EXPLANATION	PR	DEBIT	CREDIT	BALANCE

Problem AII-4A (cont'd)

	Advertising Expense				ACCOUNT NO. 655
DATE	EXPLANATION	PR	DEBIT	CREDIT	BALANCE

NOTE: For Parts 2 and 3, journalizing and posting, continue journalizing the transactions in the journals provided in Problem AII-3A.

Part 5

Trial Balance	Debit	Credit

Problem AII-4A (concl'd.)

Schedule of Accounts Receivable

Schedule of Accounts Payable

Analysis component:

Name: _____

Problem AII-5A

Parts 1, 2, 3

Sales Journal					Page 3
Date	Account Debited	Invoice Number	PR	Accounts Receivable Dr. Sales Cr.	Cost of Goods Sold Dr. Merchandise Inventory Cr.
2023					
Oct. 6	M. Craig	913	√	3,300	1,600
12	V. Foresman	914	√	3,650	1,900
15	A. Ihrig	915	√	3,100	1,700

Purchases Journal								Page 2
Date	Account	Date of Invoice	Terms	PR	Accounts Payable Cr.	Merch. Inventory Dr.	Office Supplies Dr.	Other Accounts Dr.
2023								
Oct. 2	Shore Co.	Oct. 2	2/10,n/60	√	3,200	3,200		
5	Brown Sup.	Oct. 3	n/10,EOM	√	1,300	1,300		
15	Shore Co.	Oct. 15	2/10,n/60	√	3,990	3,990		
15	Sunshine Co	Oct. 15	2/10,n/60	√	2,650	2,650		

Problem AII-5A (cont'd.)

Cash Receipts Journal									Page 3
Date	Account Credited	PR	Explanation	Cash Dr.	Sales Disc. Dr.	Accts. Rec. Cr.	Sales Cr.	Other Accts. Cr.	COGS Dr. Merch. Inv. Cr.
2023									
Oct. 2	B. Grigsby	√	Inv. 09/23	4,116	84	4,200			
15	Sales		Cash sales	38,830			38,830		21,400
15	M. Craig	√	Inv. 10/6	2,401	49	2,450			

Cash Disbursements Journal								Page 4
Date	Ch. No.	Payee	Account Debited	PR	Cash Cr.	Merch. Inventory Cr.	Other Accounts Dr.	Accounts Payable Dr.
2023								
Oct. 2	619	Omni Realty	Rent Exp.	640	2,250		2,250	
6	620	Fireside Co.	Fireside Co.	√	3,724	76		3,800
12	621	Shore Co.	Shore Co.	√	3,136	64		3,200
15	622	Jamie Green	Sales Sal. Exp.	621	2,020		2,020	

Problem AII-5A (cont'd.)

GENERAL JOURNAL

Page 2

Date		Account Titles and Explanation	PR	Debit	Credit
2023					
Oct.	4	Accounts Payable—Fireside Company	201/√	460	
		Merchandise Inventory	119		460
		Received a credit memo for returns.			
	9	Sales Returns and Allowances	414	850	
		Accounts Receivable—Marge Craig	106/√		850
		Issued a credit memorandum.			
	9	Merchandise Inventory	119	430	
		Cost of Goods Sold	502		430
		Merchandise returned to inventory.			

ACCOUNTS RECEIVABLE SUBLEDGER
Marge Craig

DATE	EXPLANATION	PR	DEBIT	CREDIT	BALANCE
2023					
Oct. 6		S3	3,300		3,300
9		G2		850	2,450
15		CR3		2,450	-0-

Vickie Foresman

DATE	EXPLANATION	PR	DEBIT	CREDIT	BALANCE
2023					
Oct. 12		S3	3,650		3,650

Problem AII-5A (cont'd.)

Parts 2 and 3

Bill Grigsby

DATE		EXPLANATION	PR	DEBIT	CREDIT	BALANCE
2023						
Sept.	23		S2	4,200		4,200
Oct.	2		CR3		4,200	-0-

Amy Ihrig

DATE		EXPLANATION	PR	DEBIT	CREDIT	BALANCE
2023						
Oct.	15		S3	3,100		3,100

ACCOUNTS PAYABLE SUBLEDGER

Fireside Company

DATE		EXPLANATION	PR	DEBIT	CREDIT	BALANCE
2023						
Sept.	28		P1		4,260	4,260
Oct.	4		G2	460		3,800
	6		CD4	3,800		-0-

Brown Supply Company

DATE		EXPLANATION	PR	DEBIT	CREDIT	BALANCE
2023						
Oct.	5		P2		1,300	1,300

Sunshine Company

DATE		EXPLANATION	PR	DEBIT	CREDIT	BALANCE
2023						
Oct.	15		P2		2,650	2,650

Problem AII-5A (cont'd.)

Parts 2 and 3 (Cont'd.)

Shore Company

DATE	EXPLANATION	PR	DEBIT	CREDIT	BALANCE
2023					
Oct. 2		P2		3,200	3,200
12		CD4	3,200		-0-
15		P2		3,990	3,990

Parts 2 and 3   **GENERAL LEDGER**

Cash   ACCOUNT NO. 101

DATE	EXPLANATION	PR	DEBIT	CREDIT	BALANCE
2023					
Sept. 30	Balance				5,361

Accounts Receivable   ACCOUNT NO. 106

DATE	EXPLANATION	PR	DEBIT	CREDIT	BALANCE
2023					
Sept. 30	Balance				4,200
Oct. 9		G2		850	3,350

Merchandise Inventory   ACCOUNT NO. 119

DATE	EXPLANATION	PR	DEBIT	CREDIT	BALANCE
2023					
Sept. 30	Balance				66,970
Oct. 4		G2		460	66,510
9		G2	430		66,940

Problem AII-5A (cont'd.)

Office Supplies — ACCOUNT NO. 124

DATE	EXPLANATION	PR	DEBIT	CREDIT	BALANCE
2023					
Sept. 30	Balance				607

Store Supplies — ACCOUNT NO. 125

DATE	EXPLANATION	PR	DEBIT	CREDIT	BALANCE
2023					
Sept. 30	Balance				346

Store Equipment — ACCOUNT NO. 165

DATE	EXPLANATION	PR	DEBIT	CREDIT	BALANCE
2023					
Sept. 30	Balance				42,129

Accumulated Depreciation, Store Equipment — ACCOUNT NO. 166

DATE	EXPLANATION	PR	DEBIT	CREDIT	BALANCE
2023					
Sept. 30	Balance				9,153

Accounts Payable — ACCOUNT NO. 201

DATE	EXPLANATION	PR	DEBIT	CREDIT	BALANCE
2023					
Sept. 30	Balance				4,260
Oct. 4		G2	460		3,800

Ken Shaw, Capital — ACCOUNT NO. 301

DATE	EXPLANATION	PR	DEBIT	CREDIT	BALANCE
2023					
Sept. 30	Balance				106,200

Problem AII-5A (cont'd.)

Ken Shaw, Withdrawals   ACCOUNT NO. 302

DATE	EXPLANATION	PR	DEBIT	CREDIT	BALANCE
2023					

Sales   ACCOUNT NO. 413

DATE	EXPLANATION	PR	DEBIT	CREDIT	BALANCE
2023					

Sales Returns and Allowances   ACCOUNT NO. 414

DATE	EXPLANATION	PR	DEBIT	CREDIT	BALANCE
2023					
Oct. 9		G2	850		850

Sales Discounts   ACCOUNT NO. 415

DATE	EXPLANATION	PR	DEBIT	CREDIT	BALANCE
2023					

Cost of Goods Sold   ACCOUNT NO. 502

DATE	EXPLANATION	PR	DEBIT	CREDIT	BALANCE
2023					
Oct. 9		G2		430	(430)

Sales Salaries Expense   ACCOUNT NO. 621

DATE	EXPLANATION	PR	DEBIT	CREDIT	BALANCE
2023					
Oct. 15		CD4	2,020		2,020

Rent Expense   ACCOUNT NO. 640

DATE	EXPLANATION	PR	DEBIT	CREDIT	BALANCE
2023					
Oct. 2		CD4	2,250		2,250

Problem AII-5A (cont'd.)

	Utilities Expense			ACCOUNT NO. 690	
DATE	EXPLANATION	PR	DEBIT	CREDIT	BALANCE
2023					

Part 4

SASKAN ENTERPRISES
Trial Balance
October 31, 2023

Appendix II

Name: _____

Problem AII-5A (concl'd.)

Part 4

SASKAN ENTERPRISES

Schedule of Accounts Receivable

October 31, 2023

SASKAN ENTERPRISES

Schedule of Accounts Payable

October 31, 2023

Problem AII-6A

Sales Journal						Page
Date	Account Debited	Invoice Number	PR	Accounts Receivable Dr. Sales Cr.	PR	Cost of Goods Sold Dr. Merch. Inventory Cr.

Purchases Journal									Page
Date	Account Credited	Date of Invoice	Terms	PR	Accts. Payable Cr.	PR	Merch. Inventory Dr.	Office Supplies Dr.	Other Accounts Dr.

NOTE: An additional PR column has been added to both journals to facilitate the referencing of inventory entries into the inventory subsidiary ledger.

Problem AII-6A (concl'd.)

Inventory Subledger Record – FIFO Perpetual

Date	PR	Purchases	Sales (at cost)	Inventory Balance

Note: An additional PR column has been added to the Inventory Subledger Record to facilitate referencing of inventory entries.

*Problem AII-7A

Note: Since posting to the General Ledger was not a requirement in this problem, posting references are shown for values posted to the subledgers only.

	Sales Journal			Page
Date	Account Debited	Invoice No.	PR	Accounts Receivable Dr. Sales Cr.

	Cash Receipts Journal							Page
Date	Account Credited	Explanation	PR	Cash Dr.	Sales Disc. Dr.	Accts. Rec. Cr.	Sales Cr.	Other Accts. Cr.

Problem AII-7A (cont'd.)

Date	Account Credited	Date of Invoice	Terms	PR	Accts. Payable Cr.	Purchases Dr.	Office Supplies Dr.	Other Accts. Dr.	

Purchases Journal — Page

Date	Account Credited	Date of Invoice	Terms	PR	Accts. Payable Cr.	Purchases Dr.	Office Supplies Dr.	Other Accts. Dr.

Cash Disbursements Journal — Page

Date	Ch. No.	Payee	Account Debited	PR	Cash Cr.	Purch. Disc. Cr.	Other Accounts Dr.	Accts. Payable Dr.

GENERAL JOURNAL — Page____

Date	Account Titles and Explanation	PR	Debit	Credit

Problem AII-7A (cont'd.)

ACCOUNTS RECEIVABLE SUBLEDGER

Paul Abrams ACCOUNT NO. 106-1

DATE	EXPLANATION	PR	DEBIT	CREDIT	BALANCE

Linda Hobart ACCOUNT NO. 106-2

DATE	EXPLANATION	PR	DEBIT	CREDIT	BALANCE

Kelly Schaefer ACCOUNT NO. 106-3

DATE	EXPLANATION	PR	DEBIT	CREDIT	BALANCE

Fundamental Accounting Principles, 17ce, Working Papers

*Problem AII-7A (cont'd)

ACCOUNTS PAYABLE SUBLEDGER

Frank's Supply   ACCOUNT NO. 201-1

DATE	EXPLANATION	PR	DEBIT	CREDIT	BALANCE

Baskin Company   ACCOUNT NO. 201-2

DATE	EXPLANATION	PR	DEBIT	CREDIT	BALANCE

Sprocket Company   ACCOUNT NO. 201-3

DATE	EXPLANATION	PR	DEBIT	CREDIT	BALANCE

Eau Claire Inc.   ACCOUNT NO. 201-4

DATE	EXPLANATION	PR	DEBIT	CREDIT	BALANCE

*Problem AII-7A (cont'd)

Parts 1, 2, 3, 4   **GENERAL LEDGER**

Cash   **ACCOUNT NO. 101**

DATE	EXPLANATION	PR	DEBIT	CREDIT	BALANCE
2023					
Mar.31	Balance Forward				167,000

Accounts Receivable   **ACCOUNT NO. 106**

DATE	EXPLANATION	PR	DEBIT	CREDIT	BALANCE

Merchandise Inventory   **ACCOUNT NO. 119**

DATE	EXPLANATION	PR	DEBIT	CREDIT	BALANCE
2023					
Mar.31	Balance Forward				105,000

Office Supplies   **ACCOUNT NO. 124**

DATE	EXPLANATION	PR	DEBIT	CREDIT	BALANCE

Store Supplies   **ACCOUNT NO. 125**

DATE	EXPLANATION	PR	DEBIT	CREDIT	BALANCE

Store Equipment   **ACCOUNT NO. 165**

DATE	EXPLANATION	PR	DEBIT	CREDIT	BALANCE

Accounts Payable   **ACCOUNT NO. 201**

DATE	EXPLANATION	PR	DEBIT	CREDIT	BALANCE

*Problem AII-7A (cont'd)

Long-Term Notes Payable — ACCOUNT NO. 251

DATE	EXPLANATION	PR	DEBIT	CREDIT	BALANCE
2023					
Mar.31	Balance Forward				167,000

Jeff Newton, Capital — ACCOUNT NO. 301

DATE	EXPLANATION	PR	DEBIT	CREDIT	BALANCE
2023					
Mar.31					105,000

Sales — ACCOUNT NO. 413

DATE	EXPLANATION	PR	DEBIT	CREDIT	BALANCE

Sales Discounts — ACCOUNT NO. 415

DATE	EXPLANATION	PR	DEBIT	CREDIT	BALANCE

Purchases — ACCOUNT NO. 505

DATE	EXPLANATION	PR	DEBIT	CREDIT	BALANCE

Purchases Discounts — ACCOUNT NO. 506

DATE	EXPLANATION	PR	DEBIT	CREDIT	BALANCE

Purchases Returns and Allowances — ACCOUNT NO. 507

DATE	EXPLANATION	PR	DEBIT	CREDIT	BALANCE

*Problem AII-7A (cont'd)

Sales Salaries Expense   ACCOUNT NO. 621

DATE	EXPLANATION	PR	DEBIT	CREDIT	BALANCE

Advertising Expense   ACCOUNT NO. 655

DATE	EXPLANATION	PR	DEBIT	CREDIT	BALANCE

Part 5

Schedule of Accounts Receivable

Schedule of Accounts Payable

*Problem AII-7A (concl'd)

Part 5

		Debit	Credit
	Trial Balance		

Problem AII-8A

Parts 1 and 2

						Page 3
				Sales Journal		
Date	Account Debited	Invoice Number	PR	Accounts Receivable Dr. Sales Cr.	Cost of Goods Sold Dr. Merchandise Inventory Cr.	

									Page 2
				Purchases Journal					
Date	Account	Date of Invoice	Terms	PR	Accounts Payable Cr.	Merch. Inventory Dr.	Office Supplies Dr.	Other Accounts Dr.	

Name: _____

Problem AII-8A (cont'd.)

Parts 1 and 2 - continued

Cash Receipts Journal										**Page 3**
Date	Account Credited	Explanation	P R	Cash Dr.	Sales Disc. Dr.	Accts. Rec. Cr.	Sales Cr.	Other Accts. Cr.	COGS Dr. Merch. Inv. Cr.	

Cash Payments Journal								**Page 4**
Date	Chq No.	Payee	Account Debited	PR	Cash Cr.	Merch. Inventory Cr.	Other Accounts Dr.	Accounts Payable Dr.

Problem AII-8A (cont'd.)

Parts 1 and 2 - continued

GENERAL JOURNAL   Page 2

Date		Account Titles and Explanation	PR	Debit	Credit

Problem AII—8A (cont'd)

Parts 1 and 2   **GENERAL LEDGER**

Cash   ACCOUNT NO. 101

DATE	EXPLANATION	PR	DEBIT	CREDIT	BALANCE

Accounts Receivable   ACCOUNT NO. 106

DATE	EXPLANATION	PR	DEBIT	CREDIT	BALANCE

Merchandise Inventory   ACCOUNT NO. 119

DATE	EXPLANATION	PR	DEBIT	CREDIT	BALANCE
Mar. 1	Balance Forward				10,000

Office Supplies   ACCOUNT NO. 124

DATE	EXPLANATION	PR	DEBIT	CREDIT	BALANCE

Store Supplies   ACCOUNT NO. 125

DATE	EXPLANATION	PR	DEBIT	CREDIT	BALANCE

Office Equipment   ACCOUNT NO. 163

DATE	EXPLANATION	PR	DEBIT	CREDIT	BALANCE

Problem AII—8A (cont'd)

Accounts Payable · ACCOUNT NO. 201

DATE	EXPLANATION	PR	DEBIT	CREDIT	BALANCE

Long-Term Notes Payable · ACCOUNT NO. 251

DATE	EXPLANATION	PR	DEBIT	CREDIT	BALANCE

Z. Church, Capital · ACCOUNT NO. 301

DATE	EXPLANATION	PR	DEBIT	CREDIT	BALANCE
Mar. 1	Balance Forward				10,000

Sales · ACCOUNT NO. 413

DATE	EXPLANATION	PR	DEBIT	CREDIT	BALANCE

Sales Discounts · ACCOUNT NO. 415

DATE	EXPLANATION	PR	DEBIT	CREDIT	BALANCE

Cost of Goods Sold · ACCOUNT NO. 502

DATE	EXPLANATION	PR	DEBIT	CREDIT	BALANCE

Problem AII-8A (cont'd)

Sales Salaries Expense — ACCOUNT NO. 621

DATE	EXPLANATION	PR	DEBIT	CREDIT	BALANCE

ACCOUNTS RECEIVABLE SUBLEDGER

Jovita Albany — ACCOUNT NO. 106-1

DATE	EXPLANATION	PR	DEBIT	CREDIT	BALANCE

Min Cho — ACCOUNT NO. 106-2

DATE	EXPLANATION	PR	DEBIT	CREDIT	BALANCE

Linda Witt — ACCOUNT NO. 106-3

DATE	EXPLANATION	PR	DEBIT	CREDIT	BALANCE

Problem AII-8A (cont'd)

ACCOUNTS PAYABLE SUBLEDGER

Gabel Company   ACCOUNT NO. 201-1

DATE	EXPLANATION	PR	DEBIT	CREDIT	BALANCE

Van Industries   ACCOUNT NO. 201-2

DATE	EXPLANATION	PR	DEBIT	CREDIT	BALANCE

Spell Supply   ACCOUNT NO. 201-3

DATE	EXPLANATION	PR	DEBIT	CREDIT	BALANCE

CD Company   ACCOUNT NO. 201-4

DATE	EXPLANATION	PR	DEBIT	CREDIT	BALANCE

Fundamental Accounting Principles, 17ce, Working Papers

Problem AII-8A (cont'd)

Part 3 (a)

Trial Balance	Debit	Credit

Name: _____

Problem AII-8A (concl'd.)

Part 3 (b)

Schedule of Accounts Receivable

Schedule of Accounts Payable

Problem AII-1B

	Special Journal			Subledger	
Sales............................	S		Accounts Receivable		AR
Purchases......................	P		Accounts Payable.............		AP
Cash Receipts.................	CR		Merchandise Inventory....		MI
Cash Disbursements.......	CD		No Effect.........................		NE
General Journal.............	G				

Date	Transaction	Special Journal	Subledger
May 1	The owner invested an automobile into the business.		
2	Sold merchandise and received cash.		
3	Purchased merchandise inventory on credit; terms 1/5, n/30.		
4	Sold merchandise on credit.		
5	The customer of May 4 returned defective merchandise; the merchandise was scrapped.		
6	Regarding the May 3 purchase, received a credit memo from the supplier granting an allowance.		
15	Paid mid-month salaries.		
17	Purchased office supplies on credit; terms n/30.		
19	Paid for the balance owing on the May 3 purchase.		
22	Received payment on the May 4 sale.		
25	Borrowed money from bank.		
29	Purchased merchandise inventory; paid cash.		
30	Accrued interest income.		
30	Closed all revenue accounts to the Income Summary account.		

Problem AII-2B

Sales Journal					Page S1
Date	Account Debited	Invoice Number	PR	Accounts Receivable Dr. Sales Cr.	Cost of Goods Sold Dr. Merchandise Inventory Cr.

Cash Receipts Journal									Page CR1
Date	Accounts Credited	PR	Explanation	Cash Dr.	Sales Disc. Dr.	Accts. Rec. Cr.	Sales Cr.	Other Accts. Cr.	COGS Dr. Merch. Inv. Cr.

Purchases Journal								Page P1
Date	Account Credited	Date of Invoice	Terms	PR	Accounts Payable Cr.	Merch. Inventory Dr.	Office Supplies Dr.	Other Accounts Dr.

Cash Disbursements Journal								Page CD1
Date	Ch. No.	Payee	Account Debited	PR	Cash Cr.	Merch. Inventory Cr.	Other Accounts Dr.	Accounts Payable Dr.

Problem AII-2B (concl'd.)

GENERAL JOURNAL   Page ____

Date	Account Titles and Explanation	PR	Debit	Credit

Problem AII-3B

Part 1   ACCOUNTS RECEIVABLE SUBLEDGER

Kelly Grody   ACCOUNT NO. 106-1

DATE	EXPLANATION	PR	DEBIT	CREDIT	BALANCE

Karen Harden   ACCOUNT NO. 106-2

DATE	EXPLANATION	PR	DEBIT	CREDIT	BALANCE

Paul Kane   ACCOUNT NO. 106-3

DATE	EXPLANATION	PR	DEBIT	CREDIT	BALANCE

Problem AII-3B (cont'd.)

Part 2   ACCOUNTS PAYABLE SUBLEDGER
                                Beech Company   ACCOUNT NO. 201-1

DATE	EXPLANATION	PR	DEBIT	CREDIT	BALANCE

Blackwater Inc.   ACCOUNT NO. 201-2

DATE	EXPLANATION	PR	DEBIT	CREDIT	BALANCE

Poppe's Supply   ACCOUNT NO. 201-3

DATE	EXPLANATION	PR	DEBIT	CREDIT	BALANCE

Sprague Company   ACCOUNT NO. 201-4

DATE	EXPLANATION	PR	DEBIT	CREDIT	BALANCE

Part 3

			Sales Journal		Page 3
Date	Account Debited	Invoice Number	PR	Accounts Receivable Dr. Sales Cr.	Cost of Goods Sold Dr. Merchandise Inventory Cr.

Problem AII-3B (cont'd.)

Cash Receipts Journal									Page 3
Date	Account Credited	Explanation	PR	Cash Dr.	Sales Disc. Dr.	Accts. Rec. Cr.	Sales Cr.	Other Accts. Cr.	COGS Dr. Merch. Inv. Cr.

Purchases Journal								Page 3
Date	Account Credited	Date of Invoice	Terms	PR	Accounts Payable Cr.	Merch. Inventory Dr.	Office Supplies Dr.	Other Accounts Dr.

Cash Disbursements Journal								Page 3
Date	Ch. No.	Payee	Account Debited	PR	Cash Cr.	Merch. Inventory Cr.	Other Accounts Dr.	Accounts Payable Dr.

Problem AII-3B (concl'd.)

GENERAL JOURNAL   Page____

Date	Account Titles and Explanation	PR	Debit	Credit

Problem AII-4B

Part 1, 4   GENERAL LEDGER

Cash   ACCOUNT NO. 101

DATE	EXPLANATION	PR	DEBIT	CREDIT	BALANCE
2023					
Jun. 30	Balance brought forward				190,000

Accounts Receivable   ACCOUNT NO. 106

DATE	EXPLANATION	PR	DEBIT	CREDIT	BALANCE

Merchandise Inventory   ACCOUNT NO. 119

DATE	EXPLANATION	PR	DEBIT	CREDIT	BALANCE
2023					
Jun. 30	Balance brought forward				334,000

Problem AII-4B (cont'd.)

Office Supplies   ACCOUNT NO. 124

DATE	EXPLANATION	PR	DEBIT	CREDIT	BALANCE

Store Supplies   ACCOUNT NO. 125

DATE	EXPLANATION	PR	DEBIT	CREDIT	BALANCE

Store Equipment   ACCOUNT NO. 165

DATE	EXPLANATION	PR	DEBIT	CREDIT	BALANCE

Accounts Payable   ACCOUNT NO. 201

DATE	EXPLANATION	PR	DEBIT	CREDIT	BALANCE

Long-Term Notes Payable   ACCOUNT NO. 251

DATE	EXPLANATION	PR	DEBIT	CREDIT	BALANCE
2023					
Jun. 30	Balance brought forward				334,000

Gene Duncan, Capital   ACCOUNT NO. 301

DATE	EXPLANATION	PR	DEBIT	CREDIT	BALANCE
2023					
Jun. 30	Balance brought forward				190,000

Problem AII-4B (cont'd.)

Sales   ACCOUNT NO. 413

DATE	EXPLANATION	PR	DEBIT	CREDIT	BALANCE

Sales Discounts   ACCOUNT NO. 415

DATE	EXPLANATION	PR	DEBIT	CREDIT	BALANCE

Cost of Goods Sold   ACCOUNT NO. 502

DATE	EXPLANATION	PR	DEBIT	CREDIT	BALANCE

Sales Salaries Expense   ACCOUNT NO. 621

DATE	EXPLANATION	PR	DEBIT	CREDIT	BALANCE

Advertising Expense   ACCOUNT NO. 655

DATE	EXPLANATION	PR	DEBIT	CREDIT	BALANCE

NOTE: For Parts 2, 3, and 4, journalizing and posting, continue journalizing the transactions in the accounts provided in Problem AII-3A.

Problem AII-4B (cont'd.)

Part 5

DUNCAN INDUSTRIES
Trial Balance
July 31, 2023

	Debit	Credit

DUNCAN INDUSTRIES
Schedule of Accounts Receivable
July 31, 2023

DUNCAN INDUSTRIES
Schedule of Accounts Payable
July 31, 2023

Appendix II

Name: _____

Problem AII-4B (concl'd.)

Analysis component:

_____

_____

_____

_____

_____

_____

_____

_____

_____

_____

Problem AII-5B

Part 1

				Sales Journal	Page 3
Date	Account Debited	Invoice Number	PR	Accounts Receivable Dr. Sales Cr.	Cost of Goods Sold Dr. Merchandise Inventory Cr.
2023					
Oct. 6	M. Craig	913	√	6,600	3,600
12	H. Flatt	914	√	7,300	4,000
15	A. Izon	915	√	6,200	3,400

			Cash Receipts Journal						Page 3
Date	Account Credited	PR	Explanation	Cash Dr.	Sales Disc. Dr.	Accts. Rec. Cr.	Sales Cr.	Other Accts. Cr.	COGS Dr. Merch. Inv. Cr.
2023									
Oct. 2	J. Wildman	√	Inv. 09/23	8,232	168	8,400			
15	Sales		Cash sales	77,660			77,660		42,800
15	M. Craig	√	Inv. 10/6	4,802	98	4,900			

Copyright © 2022 by McGraw Hill Ltd.

Fundamental Accounting Principles, 17ce, Working Papers

Problem AII-5B (cont'd.)

Purchases Journal								Page 2
Date	Account Credited	Date of Invoice	Terms	PR	Accounts Payable Cr.	Merch. Inventory Dr.	Office Supplies Dr.	Other Accounts Dr.
2023								
Oct. 2	Walters Co.	10/2	2/10,n/60	√	6,400	6,400		
5	Green Supply	10/3	n/10,EOM	√	2,600	2,600		
15	Walters Co.	10/15	2/10,n/60	√	7,980	7,980		
15	Sunshine Co.	10/15	2/10,n/60	√	5,300	5,300		

Cash Disbursements Journal								Page 4
Date	Ch. No.	Payee	Account Debited	PR	Cash Cr.	Merch. Inventory Cr.	Other Accounts Dr.	Accounts Payable Dr.
2023								
Oct. 2	619	Omni Realty	Rent Exp.	640	4,500		4,500	
6	620	Fireside Co.	Fireside Co.	√	7,448	152		7,600
12	621	Walters Co.	Walters Co.	√	6,272	128		6,400
15	622	Jamie Ford	Sales Sal. Exp.	621	5,240		5,240	

Problem AII-5B (cont'd.)

GENERAL JOURNAL   Page 2

Date		Account Titles and Explanation	PR	Debit	Credit
2023					
Oct.	4	Accounts Payable—Fireside Company	201/√	920	
		Merchandise Inventory	119		920
		Received a credit memo for returns.			
	9	Sales Returns and Allowances	414	1,700	
		Accounts Receivable—Marge Craig	106/√		1,700
		Issued a credit memorandum.			

ACCOUNTS RECEIVABLE SUBLEDGER
Marge Craig

DATE		EXPLANATION	PR	DEBIT	CREDIT	BALANCE
2023						
Oct.	6		S3	6,600		6,600
	9		G2		1,700	4,900
	15		CR3		4,900	-0-

Heather Flatt

DATE		EXPLANATION	PR	DEBIT	CREDIT	BALANCE
2023						
Oct.	12		S3	7,300		7,300

Amy Izon

DATE		EXPLANATION	PR	DEBIT	CREDIT	BALANCE
2023						
Oct.	15		S3	6,200		6,200

Jan Wildman

DATE		EXPLANATION	PR	DEBIT	CREDIT	BALANCE
2023						
Sept.	23		S2	8,400		8,400
Oct.	2		CR3		8,400	-0-

ACCOUNTS PAYABLE SUBLEDGER
Fireside Company

DATE		EXPLANATION	PR	DEBIT	CREDIT	BALANCE
2023						
Sept.	28		P1		8,520	8,520
Oct.	4		G2	920		7,600
	6		CD4	7,600		-0-

Green Supply Company

DATE		EXPLANATION	PR	DEBIT	CREDIT	BALANCE
2023						
Oct.	5		P2		2,600	2,600

Sunshine Company

DATE		EXPLANATION	PR	DEBIT	CREDIT	BALANCE
2023						
Oct.	15		P2		5,300	5,300

Appendix II

Name: _____

Problem AII-5B (cont'd.)

Walters Company

DATE	EXPLANATION	PR	DEBIT	CREDIT	BALANCE
2023					
Oct. 2		P2		6,400	6,400
12		CD4	6,400		-0-
15		P2		7,980	7,980

Parts 2 and 3   **GENERAL LEDGER**

Cash   ACCOUNT NO. 101

DATE	EXPLANATION	PR	DEBIT	CREDIT	BALANCE
2023					
Sept. 30	Balance				10,722

Accounts Receivable   ACCOUNT NO. 106

DATE	EXPLANATION	PR	DEBIT	CREDIT	BALANCE
2023					
Sept. 30	Balance				8,400
Oct. 9		G2		1,700	6,700

Merchandise Inventory   ACCOUNT NO. 119

DATE	EXPLANATION	PR	DEBIT	CREDIT	BALANCE
2023					
Sept. 30	Balance				133,940
Oct. 4		G2		920	133,020

Fundamental Accounting Principles, 17ce, Working Papers

Problem AII-5B (cont'd.)

Office Supplies   ACCOUNT NO. 124

DATE	EXPLANATION	PR	DEBIT	CREDIT	BALANCE
2023					
Sept. 30	Balance				1,214

Store Supplies   ACCOUNT NO. 125

DATE	EXPLANATION	PR	DEBIT	CREDIT	BALANCE
2023					
Sept. 30	Balance				692

Store Equipment   ACCOUNT NO. 165

DATE	EXPLANATION	PR	DEBIT	CREDIT	BALANCE
2023					
Sept. 30	Balance				84,258

Accumulated Depreciation, Store Equipment   ACCOUNT NO. 166

DATE	EXPLANATION	PR	DEBIT	CREDIT	BALANCE
2023					
Sept. 30	Balance				18,306

Accounts Payable   ACCOUNT NO. 201

DATE	EXPLANATION	PR	DEBIT	CREDIT	BALANCE
2023					
Sept. 30	Balance				8,520
Oct. 4		G2	920		7,600

Name: _____

Problem AII-5B (cont'd.)

Marlee Levin, Capital — ACCOUNT NO. 301

DATE	EXPLANATION	PR	DEBIT	CREDIT	BALANCE
2023					
Sept. 30	Balance				212,400

Marlee Levin, Withdrawals — ACCOUNT NO. 302

DATE	EXPLANATION	PR	DEBIT	CREDIT	BALANCE
2023					

Sales — ACCOUNT NO. 413

DATE	EXPLANATION	PR	DEBIT	CREDIT	BALANCE
2023					

Sales Returns and Allowances — ACCOUNT NO. 414

DATE	EXPLANATION	PR	DEBIT	CREDIT	BALANCE
2023					
Oct. 9		G2	1,700		1,700

Sales Discounts — ACCOUNT NO. 415

DATE	EXPLANATION	PR	DEBIT	CREDIT	BALANCE
2023					

Cost of Goods Sold — ACCOUNT NO. 502

DATE	EXPLANATION	PR	DEBIT	CREDIT	BALANCE
2023					

Sales Salaries Expense — ACCOUNT NO. 621

DATE	EXPLANATION	PR	DEBIT	CREDIT	BALANCE
2023					
Oct. 15		CD4	5,240		5,240

Appendix II

Name: _____

Problem AII-5B (cont'd.)

Rent Expense — ACCOUNT NO. 640

DATE	EXPLANATION	PR	DEBIT	CREDIT	BALANCE
2023					
Oct. 2		CD4	4,500		4,500

Utilities Expense — ACCOUNT NO. 690

DATE	EXPLANATION	PR	DEBIT	CREDIT	BALANCE
2023					

Part 4

CHINA MOON PRODUCTS
Trial Balance
October 31, 2023

	Debit	Credit

Problem AII-5B (concl'd.)

CHINA MOON PRODUCTS
Schedule of Accounts Receivable
October 31, 2023

CHINA MOON PRODUCTS
Schedule of Accounts Payable
October 31, 2023

Problem AII-6B

				Sales Journal			Page 1
Date	Account Debited	Invoice Number	PR	Accounts Receivable Dr. Sales Cr.	PR	Cost of Goods Sold Dr. Merch. Inventory Cr.	

					Purchases Journal				Page 1
Date	Account Credited	Date of Invoice	Terms	PR	Accts. Payable Cr.	PR	Merch. Inventory Dr.	Office Supplies Dr.	Other Accounts Dr.

NOTE: An additional PR column has been added to both journals to facilitate the referencing of inventory entries into the inventory subledger.

Problem AII-6B (concl'd.)

Inventory Subledger Record – Weighted Average Perpetual

Date	PR	Purchases	Sales (at cost)	Inventory Balance

Note: An additional PR column has been added to the Inventory Subledger Record to facilitate referencing of inventory entries.

*Problem AII-7B

Note: Since posting to the General Ledger was not a requirement in this problem, posting references are shown for values posted to the subledgers only.

Sales Journal				Page
Date	Account Debited	Invoice No.	PR	Accounts Receivable Dr. Sales Cr.

Cash Receipts Journal								Page
Date	Account Credited	Explanation	PR	Cash Dr.	Sales Disc. Dr.	Accts. Rec. Cr.	Sales Cr.	Other Accts. Cr.

*Problem AII-7B (cont'd.)

Purchases Journal								Page
Date	Account Credited	Date of Invoice	Terms	PR	Accts. Payable Cr.	Purchases Dr.	Office Supplies Dr.	Other Accts. Dr.

Cash Disbursements Journal								Page
Date	Ch. No.	Payee	Account Debited	PR	Cash Cr.	Purch. Disc. Cr.	Other Accounts Dr.	Accts. Payable Dr.

GENERAL JOURNAL   Page____

Date		Account Titles and Explanation	PR	Debit	Credit

*Problem AII-7B (cont'd)

ACCOUNTS RECEIVABLE SUBLEDGER

Karen Harden   ACCOUNT NO. 106-1

DATE	EXPLANATION	PR	DEBIT	CREDIT	BALANCE

Kelly Grody   ACCOUNT NO. 106-2

DATE	EXPLANATION	PR	DEBIT	CREDIT	BALANCE

Paul Kane   ACCOUNT NO. 106-3

DATE	EXPLANATION	PR	DEBIT	CREDIT	BALANCE

Name: _____

*Problem AII-7B (cont'd)

ACCOUNTS PAYABLE SUBLEDGER

Beech Company　　　　　　　　　　　　ACCOUNT NO. 201-1

DATE	EXPLANATION	PR	DEBIT	CREDIT	BALANCE

Blackwater Inc.　　　　　　　　　　　　ACCOUNT NO. 201-2

DATE	EXPLANATION	PR	DEBIT	CREDIT	BALANCE

Poppe's Supply　　　　　　　　　　　　ACCOUNT NO. 201-3

DATE	EXPLANATION	PR	DEBIT	CREDIT	BALANCE

Sprague Company　　　　　　　　　　　　ACCOUNT NO. 201-4

DATE	EXPLANATION	PR	DEBIT	CREDIT	BALANCE

Name: _____

*Problem AII-7B (cont'd)

Parts 1, 2, 3, 4   GENERAL LEDGER

Cash   ACCOUNT NO. 101

DATE	EXPLANATION	PR	DEBIT	CREDIT	BALANCE
2023					
Jun 30	Balance Forward				190,000

Accounts Receivable   ACCOUNT NO. 106

DATE	EXPLANATION	PR	DEBIT	CREDIT	BALANCE

Merchandise Inventory   ACCOUNT NO. 119

DATE	EXPLANATION	PR	DEBIT	CREDIT	BALANCE
2023					
Jun. 30	Balance Forward				334,000

Office Supplies   ACCOUNT NO. 124

DATE	EXPLANATION	PR	DEBIT	CREDIT	BALANCE

Store Supplies   ACCOUNT NO. 125

DATE	EXPLANATION	PR	DEBIT	CREDIT	BALANCE

Store Equipment   ACCOUNT NO. 165

DATE	EXPLANATION	PR	DEBIT	CREDIT	BALANCE

Accounts Payable   ACCOUNT NO. 201

DATE	EXPLANATION	PR	DEBIT	CREDIT	BALANCE

Copyright © 2022 by McGraw Hill Ltd.
Fundamental Accounting Principles, 17ce, Working Papers

*Problem AII-7B (cont'd)

Long-Term Notes Payable   ACCOUNT NO. 251

DATE	EXPLANATION	PR	DEBIT	CREDIT	BALANCE
2023					
Jun 30	Balance Forward				334,000

Gene Duncan, Capital   ACCOUNT NO. 301

DATE	EXPLANATION	PR	DEBIT	CREDIT	BALANCE
2023					
Jun. 30					190,000

Sales   ACCOUNT NO. 413

DATE	EXPLANATION	PR	DEBIT	CREDIT	BALANCE

Sales Discounts   ACCOUNT NO. 415

DATE	EXPLANATION	PR	DEBIT	CREDIT	BALANCE

Purchases   ACCOUNT NO. 505

DATE	EXPLANATION	PR	DEBIT	CREDIT	BALANCE

Purchases Discounts   ACCOUNT NO. 506

DATE	EXPLANATION	PR	DEBIT	CREDIT	BALANCE

Purchases Returns and Allowances   ACCOUNT NO. 507

DATE	EXPLANATION	PR	DEBIT	CREDIT	BALANCE

Name: _____

*Problem AII-7B (cont'd)

Sales Salaries Expense   ACCOUNT NO. 621

DATE	EXPLANATION	PR	DEBIT	CREDIT	BALANCE

Advertising Expense   ACCOUNT NO. 655

DATE	EXPLANATION	PR	DEBIT	CREDIT	BALANCE

Part 5

Schedule of Accounts Receivable

Schedule of Accounts Payable

Name: _____

*Problem AII-7B (cont'd)

Part 5

	Debit	Credit
Trial Balance		

*Problem AII-7B (concl'd.)

Schedule of Accounts Receivable

Schedule of Accounts Payable

Problem AII-8B

Parts 1 and 2

				Sales Journal	Page 3
Date	Account Debited	Invoice Number	PR	Accounts Receivable Dr. Sales Cr.	Cost of Goods Sold Dr. Merchandise Inventory Cr.

					Purchases Journal			Page 2
Date	Account	Date of Invoice	Terms	PR	Accounts Payable Cr.	Merch. Inventory Dr.	Office Supplies Dr.	Other Accounts Dr.

Name: _____

Problem AII-8B (cont'd.)

Parts 1 and 2 - continued

Cash Receipts Journal									Page 3
Date	Account Credited	Explanation	P R	Cash Dr.	Sales Disc. Dr.	Accts. Rec. Cr.	Sales Cr.	Other Accts. Cr.	COGS Dr. Merch. Inv. Cr.

Cash Payments Journal								Page 4
Date	Chq No.	Payee	Account Debited	PR	Cash Cr.	Merch. Inventory Cr.	Other Accounts Dr.	Accounts Payable Dr.

Problem AII-8B (cont'd.)

Parts 1 and 2 - continued

GENERAL JOURNAL   Page 2

Date		Account Titles and Explanation	PR	Debit	Credit

Problem AII—8B (cont'd)

Parts 1 and 2   GENERAL LEDGER

Cash   ACCOUNT NO. 101

DATE	EXPLANATION	PR	DEBIT	CREDIT	BALANCE

Accounts Receivable   ACCOUNT NO. 106

DATE	EXPLANATION	PR	DEBIT	CREDIT	BALANCE

Merchandise Inventory   ACCOUNT NO. 119

DATE	EXPLANATION	PR	DEBIT	CREDIT	BALANCE
Nov 1					40,000

Office Supplies   ACCOUNT NO. 124

DATE	EXPLANATION	PR	DEBIT	CREDIT	BALANCE

Store Supplies   ACCOUNT NO. 125

DATE	EXPLANATION	PR	DEBIT	CREDIT	BALANCE

Office Equipment   ACCOUNT NO. 163

DATE	EXPLANATION	PR	DEBIT	CREDIT	BALANCE

Name: _____

Problem AII—8B (cont'd)

Accounts Payable   ACCOUNT NO. 201

DATE	EXPLANATION	PR	DEBIT	CREDIT	BALANCE

Long-Term Notes Payable   ACCOUNT NO. 251

DATE	EXPLANATION	PR	DEBIT	CREDIT	BALANCE

C. Grassley, Capital   ACCOUNT NO. 301

DATE	EXPLANATION	PR	DEBIT	CREDIT	BALANCE

Sales   ACCOUNT NO. 413

DATE	EXPLANATION	PR	DEBIT	CREDIT	BALANCE

Sales Discounts   ACCOUNT NO. 415

DATE	EXPLANATION	PR	DEBIT	CREDIT	BALANCE

Cost of Goods Sold   ACCOUNT NO. 502

DATE	EXPLANATION	PR	DEBIT	CREDIT	BALANCE

Problem AII-8B (cont'd)

Sales Salaries Expense   ACCOUNT NO. 621

DATE	EXPLANATION	PR	DEBIT	CREDIT	BALANCE

ACCOUNTS RECEIVABLE SUBLEDGER

Carlos Mantel   ACCOUNT NO. 106-1

DATE	EXPLANATION	PR	DEBIT	CREDIT	BALANCE

Cyd Rounder   ACCOUNT NO. 106-2

DATE	EXPLANATION	PR	DEBIT	CREDIT	BALANCE

Tori Tripp   ACCOUNT NO. 106-3

DATE	EXPLANATION	PR	DEBIT	CREDIT	BALANCE

Fundamental Accounting Principles, 17ce, Working Papers

Problem AII-8B (cont'd)

ACCOUNTS PAYABLE SUBLEDGER

Grebe Company   ACCOUNT NO. 201-1

DATE	EXPLANATION	PR	DEBIT	CREDIT	BALANCE

BLR Industries   ACCOUNT NO. 201-2

DATE	EXPLANATION	PR	DEBIT	CREDIT	BALANCE

Brun Supply   ACCOUNT NO. 201-3

DATE	EXPLANATION	PR	DEBIT	CREDIT	BALANCE

Lo Company   ACCOUNT NO. 201-4

DATE	EXPLANATION	PR	DEBIT	CREDIT	BALANCE

Part 3 (a)

	Debit	Credit
Trial Balance		

	Debit	Credit

Name: _____

Problem AII-8B (concl'd.)

Part 3 (b)

Schedule of Accounts Receivable		

Schedule of Accounts Payable		

Comprehensive Problem

Alpine Company - Perpetual

		Sales Journal				Page 2
Date	Account Debited	Invoice Number	PR	Accounts Receivable Dr. Sales Cr.		Cost of Goods Sold Dr. Merchandise Inventory Cr.

		Purchases Journal						Page 2
Date	Account Credited	Date of Invoice	Terms	PR	Accounts Payable Cr.	Merch. Inventory Dr.	Office Supplies Dr.	Other Accounts Dr.

		Cash Receipts Journal							Page 2
Date	Account Credited	Explanation	PR	Cash Dr.	Sales Disc. Dr.	Accts. Rec. Cr.	Sales Cr.	Other Accts. Cr.	COGS Dr. Merch. Inv. Cr.

Comprehensive Problem

Alpine Company - Perpetual (Continued)

						Cash Disbursements Journal			Page 2
Date	Ch. No.	Payee	Account Debited	PR	Cash Cr.	Merch. Inventory Cr.	Other Accounts Dr.	Accounts Payable Dr.

GENERAL JOURNAL
Page 3

Date		Account Titles and Explanation	PR	Debit	Credit

Comprehensive Problem

Alpine Company - Perpetual (Continued)

GENERAL JOURNAL
Page 3

Date	Account Titles and Explanation	PR	Debit	Credit

Comprehensive Problem

Alpine Company - Perpetual (Continued)

Date		Account Titles and Explanation	PR	Debit	Credit

Comprehensive Problem

Alpine Company - Perpetual (Continued)

Cash   ACCOUNT NO. 101

DATE	EXPLANATION	PR	DEBIT	CREDIT	BALANCE
2023					
Apr. 30	Balance				50,247

Accounts Receivable   ACCOUNT NO. 106

DATE	EXPLANATION	PR	DEBIT	CREDIT	BALANCE
2023					
Apr. 30	Balance				4,730

Merchandise Inventory   ACCOUNT NO. 119

DATE	EXPLANATION	PR	DEBIT	CREDIT	BALANCE
2023					
Apr. 30	Balance				220,080

Office Supplies   ACCOUNT NO. 124

DATE	EXPLANATION	PR	DEBIT	CREDIT	BALANCE
2023					
Apr. 30	Balance				430

Store Supplies   ACCOUNT NO. 125

DATE	EXPLANATION	PR	DEBIT	CREDIT	BALANCE
2023					
Apr. 30	Balance				2,447

Fundamental Accounting Principles, 17ce, Working Papers

Comprehensive Problem

Alpine Company - Perpetual (Continued)

Prepaid Insurance — ACCOUNT NO. 128

DATE	EXPLANATION	PR	DEBIT	CREDIT	BALANCE
2023					
Apr. 30	Balance				3,318

Office Equipment — ACCOUNT NO. 163

DATE	EXPLANATION	PR	DEBIT	CREDIT	BALANCE
2023					
Apr. 30	Balance				22,470

Accumulated Depreciation, Office Equipment — ACCOUNT NO. 164

DATE	EXPLANATION	PR	DEBIT	CREDIT	BALANCE
2023					
Apr. 30	Balance				9,898

Store Equipment — ACCOUNT NO. 165

DATE	EXPLANATION	PR	DEBIT	CREDIT	BALANCE
2023					
Apr. 30	Balance				38,920

Accumulated Depreciation, Store Equipment — ACCOUNT NO. 166

DATE	EXPLANATION	PR	DEBIT	CREDIT	BALANCE
2023					
Apr. 30	Balance				17,556

Comprehensive Problem

Alpine Company - Perpetual (Continued)

Accounts Payable ACCOUNT NO. 201

DATE	EXPLANATION	PR	DEBIT	CREDIT	BALANCE
2023					
Apr. 30	Balance				7,100

Clint Barry, Capital ACCOUNT NO. 301

DATE	EXPLANATION	PR	DEBIT	CREDIT	BALANCE
2023					
Apr. 30	Balance				308,088

Clint Barry, Withdrawals ACCOUNT NO. 302

DATE	EXPLANATION	PR	DEBIT	CREDIT	BALANCE
2023					

Sales ACCOUNT NO. 413

DATE	EXPLANATION	PR	DEBIT	CREDIT	BALANCE

Sales Discounts ACCOUNT NO. 414

DATE	EXPLANATION	PR	DEBIT	CREDIT	BALANCE

Comprehensive Problem

Alpine Company - Perpetual (Continued)

Sales Returns and Allowances — ACCOUNT NO. 415

DATE	EXPLANATION	PR	DEBIT	CREDIT	BALANCE

Cost of Goods Sold — ACCOUNT NO. 502

DATE	EXPLANATION	PR	DEBIT	CREDIT	BALANCE

Depreciation Expense, Office Equipment — ACCOUNT NO. 612

DATE	EXPLANATION	PR	DEBIT	CREDIT	BALANCE

Depreciation Expense, Store Equipment — ACCOUNT NO. 613

DATE	EXPLANATION	PR	DEBIT	CREDIT	BALANCE

Office Salaries Expense — ACCOUNT NO. 620

DATE	EXPLANATION	PR	DEBIT	CREDIT	BALANCE

Name: _____

Comprehensive Problem

Alpine Company - Perpetual (Continued)

Sales Salaries Expense — ACCOUNT NO. 621

DATE	EXPLANATION	PR	DEBIT	CREDIT	BALANCE

Insurance Expense — ACCOUNT NO. 637

DATE	EXPLANATION	PR	DEBIT	CREDIT	BALANCE

Rent Expense, Office Space — ACCOUNT NO. 641

DATE	EXPLANATION	PR	DEBIT	CREDIT	BALANCE

Rent Expense, Selling Space — ACCOUNT NO. 642

DATE	EXPLANATION	PR	DEBIT	CREDIT	BALANCE

Office Supplies Expense — ACCOUNT NO. 650

DATE	EXPLANATION	PR	DEBIT	CREDIT	BALANCE

Comprehensive Problem

Alpine Company - Perpetual (Continued)

Store Supplies Expense   ACCOUNT NO. 651

DATE	EXPLANATION	PR	DEBIT	CREDIT	BALANCE

Utilities Expense   ACCOUNT NO. 690

DATE	EXPLANATION	PR	DEBIT	CREDIT	BALANCE

Income Summary   ACCOUNT NO. 901

DATE	EXPLANATION	PR	DEBIT	CREDIT	BALANCE

ACCOUNTS RECEIVABLE LEDGER

NAME   Deaver Corp.

DATE	EXPLANATION	PR	DEBIT	CREDIT	BALANCE
2023					

NAME   Essex Company

DATE	EXPLANATION	PR	DEBIT	CREDIT	BALANCE
2023					

NAME   Nabors Inc.

DATE	EXPLANATION	PR	DEBIT	CREDIT	BALANCE
2023					
Apr. 30	Balance	S2	4,730		4,730

Comprehensive Problem

Alpine Company - Perpetual (Continued)

NAME   Oscar Services.

DATE	EXPLANATION	PR	DEBIT	CREDIT	BALANCE
2023					

ACCOUNTS PAYABLE LEDGER

NAME   Chandler Corp.

DATE	EXPLANATION	PR	DEBIT	CREDIT	BALANCE
2023					

NAME   Gale Inc.

DATE	EXPLANATION	PR	DEBIT	CREDIT	BALANCE
2023					

NAME   Parkay Products

DATE	EXPLANATION	PR	DEBIT	CREDIT	BALANCE
2023					
Apr. 30	Balance	P2		7,100	7,100

NAME   Thompson Supply Co.

DATE	EXPLANATION	PR	DEBIT	CREDIT	BALANCE
2023					

Comprehensive Problem

Alpine Company - Perpetual (Continued)

Alpine Company
Work Sheet
For Month Ended May 31, 2023

Account Titles	Trial Balance		Adjustments		Income Statement		Balance Sheet and Statement of Changes in Equity	
	Debit	Credit	Debit	Credit	Debit	Credit	Debit	Credit

Appendix II

Comprehensive Problem

Alpine Company - Perpetual (Continued)

Alpine Company			
Income Statement			
For Month Ended May 31, 2023			

Name: _____

Comprehensive Problem

Alpine Company - Perpetual (Continued)

Alpine Company
Statement of Changes in Equity
For Month Ended May 31, 2023

Alpine Company
Balance Sheet
May 31, 2023

Name: _____

Comprehensive Problem

Alpine Company - Perpetual (Concluded)

Alpine Company
Post-Closing Trial Balance
May 31, 2023

	Debit	Credit

Alpine Company
Schedule of Accounts Receivable
May 31, 2023

Alpine Company
Schedule of Accounts Payable
May 31, 2023

Comprehensive Problem

Alpine Company - Periodic

Sales Journal				Page 2
Date	Account Debited	Invoice Number	PR	Accts. Receivable Dr. Sales Cr.

Purchases Journal							Page 2	
Date	Account Credited	Date of Inv.	Terms	PR	Accts. Pay. Cr.	Purchases Dr.	Office Supplies Dr.	Other Accts. Dr.

Cash Receipts Journal								Page 2
Date	Account Credited	Explanation	PR	Cash Dr.	Sales Disc. Dr.	Accts. Rec. Cr.	Sales Cr.	Other Accts. Cr.

Comprehensive Problem

Alpine Company - Periodic (Continued)

			Cash Disbursements Journal					Page 2	
Date	Ch. No.	Payee	Account Debited	PR	Cash Cr.	Purch. Disc. Cr.	Other Accts. Dr.	Accts. Payable Dr.	

GENERAL JOURNAL   Page 3

Date		Account Titles and Explanation	PR	Debit	Credit

Comprehensive Problem

Alpine Company - Periodic (Continued)

GENERAL JOURNAL

Page 3

Date		Account Titles and Explanation	PR	Debit	Credit

Comprehensive Problem

Alpine Company - Periodic (Continued)

GENERAL LEDGER

Cash   ACCOUNT NO. 101

DATE	EXPLANATION	PR	DEBIT	CREDIT	BALANCE
2023					
Apr. 30	Balance				50,247

Accounts Receivable   ACCOUNT NO. 106

DATE	EXPLANATION	PR	DEBIT	CREDIT	BALANCE
2023					
Apr. 30	Balance				4,730

Merchandise Inventory   ACCOUNT NO. 119

DATE	EXPLANATION	PR	DEBIT	CREDIT	BALANCE
2023					
Apr. 30	Balance				220,080

Office Supplies   ACCOUNT NO. 124

DATE	EXPLANATION	PR	DEBIT	CREDIT	BALANCE
2023					
Apr. 30	Balance				430

Store Supplies   ACCOUNT NO. 125

DATE	EXPLANATION	PR	DEBIT	CREDIT	BALANCE
2023					
Apr. 30	Balance				2,447

Comprehensive Problem

Alpine Company - Periodic (Continued)

Prepaid Insurance   ACCOUNT NO. 128

DATE	EXPLANATION	PR	DEBIT	CREDIT	BALANCE
2023					
Apr. 30	Balance				3,318

Office Equipment   ACCOUNT NO. 163

DATE	EXPLANATION	PR	DEBIT	CREDIT	BALANCE
2023					
Apr. 30	Balance				22,470

Accumulated Depreciation, Office Equipment   ACCOUNT NO. 164

DATE	EXPLANATION	PR	DEBIT	CREDIT	BALANCE
2023					
Apr. 30	Balance				9,898

Store Equipment   ACCOUNT NO. 165

DATE	EXPLANATION	PR	DEBIT	CREDIT	BALANCE
2023					
Apr. 30	Balance				38,920

Accumulated Depreciation, Store Equipment   ACCOUNT NO. 166

DATE	EXPLANATION	PR	DEBIT	CREDIT	BALANCE
2023					
Apr. 30	Balance				17,556

Appendix II

Name: _____

Comprehensive Problem

Alpine Company - Periodic (Continued)

Accounts Payable   ACCOUNT NO. 201

DATE	EXPLANATION	PR	DEBIT	CREDIT	BALANCE
2023					
Apr. 30	Balance				7,100

Clint Barry, Capital   ACCOUNT NO. 301

DATE	EXPLANATION	PR	DEBIT	CREDIT	BALANCE
2023					
Apr. 30	Balance				308,088

Clint Barry, Withdrawals   ACCOUNT NO. 302

DATE	EXPLANATION	PR	DEBIT	CREDIT	BALANCE
2023					

Sales   ACCOUNT NO. 413

DATE	EXPLANATION	PR	DEBIT	CREDIT	BALANCE

Sales Discounts   ACCOUNT NO. 414

DATE	EXPLANATION	PR	DEBIT	CREDIT	BALANCE

Sales Returns and Allowances   ACCOUNT NO. 415

DATE	EXPLANATION	PR	DEBIT	CREDIT	BALANCE

Comprehensive Problem

 Alpine Company - Periodic (Continued)

Purchases					ACCOUNT NO. 505	
DATE	EXPLANATION	PR	DEBIT	CREDIT	BALANCE	

Purchases Discounts					ACCOUNT NO. 506	
DATE	EXPLANATION	PR	DEBIT	CREDIT	BALANCE	

Purchases Returns and Allowances					ACCOUNT NO. 507	
DATE	EXPLANATION	PR	DEBIT	CREDIT	BALANCE	

Depreciation Expense, Office Equipment					ACCOUNT NO. 612	
DATE	EXPLANATION	PR	DEBIT	CREDIT	BALANCE	

Depreciation Expense, Store Equipment					ACCOUNT NO. 613	
DATE	EXPLANATION	PR	DEBIT	CREDIT	BALANCE	

Office Salaries Expense					ACCOUNT NO. 620	
DATE	EXPLANATION	PR	DEBIT	CREDIT	BALANCE	

Comprehensive Problem

Alpine Company - Periodic (Continued)

Sales Salaries Expense   ACCOUNT NO. 621

DATE	EXPLANATION	PR	DEBIT	CREDIT	BALANCE

Insurance Expense   ACCOUNT NO. 637

DATE	EXPLANATION	PR	DEBIT	CREDIT	BALANCE

Rent Expense, Office Space   ACCOUNT NO. 641

DATE	EXPLANATION	PR	DEBIT	CREDIT	BALANCE

Rent Expense, Selling Space   ACCOUNT NO. 642

DATE	EXPLANATION	PR	DEBIT	CREDIT	BALANCE

Office Supplies Expense   ACCOUNT NO. 650

DATE	EXPLANATION	PR	DEBIT	CREDIT	BALANCE

Comprehensive Problem

Alpine Company - Periodic (Continued)

Store Supplies Expense   ACCOUNT NO. 651

DATE	EXPLANATION	PR	DEBIT	CREDIT	BALANCE
2023					

Utilities Expense   ACCOUNT NO. 690

DATE	EXPLANATION	PR	DEBIT	CREDIT	BALANCE
2023					

Income Summary   ACCOUNT NO. 901

DATE	EXPLANATION	PR	DEBIT	CREDIT	BALANCE

ACCOUNTS RECEIVABLE LEDGER

NAME   Deaver Corp.

DATE	EXPLANATION	PR	DEBIT	CREDIT	BALANCE

NAME   Essex Company

DATE	EXPLANATION	PR	DEBIT	CREDIT	BALANCE

NAME   Nabors Inc.

DATE	EXPLANATION	PR	DEBIT	CREDIT	BALANCE
2023					
Apr. 30	Balance	S2	4,730		4,730

Comprehensive Problem

Alpine Company - Periodic (Continued)

NAME   Oscar Services.

DATE	EXPLANATION	PR	DEBIT	CREDIT	BALANCE
2023					

ACCOUNTS PAYABLE LEDGER

NAME   Chandler Corp.

DATE	EXPLANATION	PR	DEBIT	CREDIT	BALANCE
2023					

NAME   Gale Inc.

DATE	EXPLANATION	PR	DEBIT	CREDIT	BALANCE
2023					

NAME   Parkay Products

DATE	EXPLANATION	PR	DEBIT	CREDIT	BALANCE
2023					
Apr. 30	Balance	P2		7,100	7,100

NAME   Thompson Supply Co.

DATE	EXPLANATION	PR	DEBIT	CREDIT	BALANCE

Comprehensive Problem

Alpine Company - Periodic (Continued)

Alpine Company
Work Sheet
For Month Ended May 31, 2023

Account Titles	Trial Balance		Adjustments		Income Statement		Balance Sheet and Statement of Changes in Equity	
	Debit	Credit	Debit	Credit	Debit	Credit	Debit	Credit

Name: _____

Comprehensive Problem

Alpine Company - Periodic (Continued)

Alpine Company				
Income Statement				
For Month Ended May 31, 2023				

Fundamental Accounting Principles, 17ce, Working Papers

Comprehensive Problem

Alpine Company - Periodic (Continued)

Alpine Company
Statement of Changes in Equity
For Month Ended May 31, 2023

Alpine Company
Balance Sheet
May 31, 2023

Name: _____

Comprehensive Problem

Alpine Company - Periodic (Concluded)

<table>
<tr><th colspan="3">Alpine Company</th></tr>
<tr><th colspan="3">Post-Closing Trial Balance</th></tr>
<tr><th colspan="3">May 31, 2023</th></tr>
<tr><th></th><th>Debit</th><th>Credit</th></tr>
<tr><td></td><td></td><td></td></tr>
<tr><td></td><td></td><td></td></tr>
<tr><td></td><td></td><td></td></tr>
<tr><td></td><td></td><td></td></tr>
<tr><td></td><td></td><td></td></tr>
<tr><td></td><td></td><td></td></tr>
<tr><td></td><td></td><td></td></tr>
<tr><td></td><td></td><td></td></tr>
<tr><td></td><td></td><td></td></tr>
<tr><td></td><td></td><td></td></tr>
<tr><td></td><td></td><td></td></tr>
<tr><td></td><td></td><td></td></tr>
<tr><td></td><td></td><td></td></tr>
<tr><td></td><td></td><td></td></tr>
<tr><td></td><td></td><td></td></tr>
<tr><td></td><td></td><td></td></tr>
<tr><td></td><td></td><td></td></tr>
<tr><td></td><td></td><td></td></tr>
</table>

<table>
<tr><th colspan="3">Alpine Company</th></tr>
<tr><th colspan="3">Schedule of Accounts Receivable</th></tr>
<tr><th colspan="3">May 31, 2023</th></tr>
<tr><td></td><td></td><td></td></tr>
<tr><td></td><td></td><td></td></tr>
<tr><td></td><td></td><td></td></tr>
<tr><td></td><td></td><td></td></tr>
</table>

<table>
<tr><th colspan="3">Alpine Company</th></tr>
<tr><th colspan="3">Schedule of Accounts Payable</th></tr>
<tr><th colspan="3">May 31, 2023</th></tr>
<tr><td></td><td></td><td></td></tr>
<tr><td></td><td></td><td></td></tr>
<tr><td></td><td></td><td></td></tr>
<tr><td></td><td></td><td></td></tr>
</table>